Quantitative Methods for Business

Selected Readings for Babson College

David R. Anderson I Dennis J. Sweeney
Thomas A. Williams

CENGAGE
Learning™

Australia • Brazil • Japan • Korea • Mexico • Singapore • Spain • United Kingdom • United States

**Quantitative Methods for Business:
Selected Readings for Babson College**

David R. Anderson I Dennis J. Sweeney
Thomas A. Williams

Executive Editor:
 Maureen Staudt
 Michael Stranz

Senior Project Development Manager:
 Linda de Stefano

Marketing Specialist:
 Sara Mercurio
 Lindsay Shapiro

Production/Manufacturing Manager:
 Donna M. Brown

PreMedia Supervisor:
 Joel Brennecke

Rights & Permissions Specialist:
 Kalina Hintz
 Todd Osborne

Cover Image:
 Getty Images*

For product information and technology assistance, contact us at
Cengage Learning Customer & Sales Support, 1-800-354-9706

For permission to use material from this text or product,
submit all requests online at **cengage.com/permissions**
Further permissions questions can be emailed to
permissionrequest@cengage.com

ISBN-13:978-1-111-21260-5

ISBN-10: 1-111-21260-0

Cengage Learning
5191 Natorp Boulevard
Mason, Ohio 45040
USA

Cengage Learning is a leading provider of customized learning solutions with office locations around the globe, including Singapore, the United Kingdom, Australia, Mexico, Brazil, and Japan. Locate your local office at:
international.cengage.com/region

Cengage Learning products are represented in Canada by
Nelson Education, Ltd.

For your lifelong learning solutions, visit **www.cengage.com/custom**

Visit our corporate website at **www.cengage.com**

Printed in the United States of America

Acknowledgements

The content of this text has been adapted from the following product(s):

Quantitative Methods for Business, 10th
ANDERSON/SWEENEY/WILLIAMS ISBN-10: (0-324-31260-1)
ISBN-13: (978-0-324-31260-7)

Table Of Contents

Utility and Game Theory

CONTENTS

The decision analysis situations presented in Chapter 4 often expressed consequences or payoffs in terms of monetary values. With probability information available about the outcomes of the chance events, we defined the optimal decision alternative as the one that provided the best expected monetary value. However, in some situations the decision alternative with the best expected monetary value may not be the preferred alternative. A decision maker may also wish to consider intangible factors such as risk, image, or other nonmonetary criteria in order to evaluate the decision alternatives. When monetary value does not necessarily lead to the most preferred decision, expressing the value (or worth) of a consequence in terms of its utility will permit the use of expected utility to identify the most desirable decision alternative. The discussion of utility and its application in decision analysis is presented in the first part of this chapter.

In the last part of this chapter, we introduce the topic of game theory. Game theory is the study of developing optimal strategies where two or more decision makers, usually called players, compete as adversaries. Game theory can be viewed as a relative of decision analysis. A key difference, however, is that each player selects a decision strategy not by considering the possible outcomes of a chance event, but by considering the possible strategies selected by one or more competing players.

We note here that utility and game theory are separable topics. Either or both may be studied, and it is not required that you cover one topic before the other.

5.1   THE MEANING OF UTILITY

Utility is a measure of the total worth of a particular outcome; it reflects the decision maker's attitude toward a collection of factors such as profit, loss, and risk. Researchers have found that as long as the monetary value of payoffs stays within a range that the decision maker considers reasonable, selecting the decision alternative with the best expected monetary value usually leads to selection of the most preferred decision. However, when the payoffs become extreme, most decision makers are not satisfied with the decision that simply provides the best expected monetary value.

As an example of a situation in which utility can help in selecting the best decision alternative, let us consider the problem faced by Swofford, Inc., a relatively small real estate investment firm located in Atlanta, Georgia. Swofford currently has two investment opportunities that require approximately the same cash outlay. The cash requirements necessary prohibit Swofford from making more than one investment at this time. Consequently, three possible decision alternatives may be considered.

The three decision alternatives, denoted d_1, d_2, and d_3, are

$$d_1 = \text{make investment A}$$
$$d_2 = \text{make investment B}$$
$$d_3 = \text{do not invest}$$

The monetary payoffs associated with the investment opportunities depend on the investment decision and on the direction of the real estate market during the next six months (the chance event). Real estate prices will go up, remain stable, or go down. Thus the Swofford states of nature, denoted by s_1, s_2, and s_3, are

$$s_1 = \text{real estate prices go up}$$
$$s_2 = \text{real estate prices remain stable}$$
$$s_3 = \text{real estate prices go down}$$

TABLE 5.1 PAYOFF TABLE FOR SWOFFORD, INC.

Decision Alternative	State of Nature		
	Prices Up s_1	Prices Stable s_2	Prices Down s_3
Investment A, d_1	$30,000	$20,000	−$50,000
Investment B, d_2	$50,000	−$20,000	−$30,000
Do not invest, d_3	0	0	0

Using the best information available, Swofford has estimated the profits, or payoffs, associated with each decision alternative and state-of-nature combination. The resulting payoff table is shown in Table 5.1.

The best estimate of the probability that real estate prices will go up is 0.3; the best estimate of the probability that prices will remain stable is 0.5; and the best estimate of the probability that prices will go down is 0.2. Thus the expected values for the three decision alternatives are

$$EV(d_1) = 0.3(30,000) + 0.5(20,000) \quad + 0.2(-50,000) = 9000$$
$$EV(d_2) = 0.3(50,000) + 0.5(-20,000) + 0.2(-30,000) = -1000$$
$$EV(d_3) = 0.3(0) \quad\quad + 0.5(0) \quad\quad + 0.2(0) \quad\quad = 0$$

Using the expected value approach, the optimal decision is to select investment A with an expected monetary value of $9000. Is it really the best decision alternative? Let us consider some other relevant factors that relate to Swofford's capability for absorbing the loss of $50,000 if investment A is made and prices actually go down.

Actually, Swofford's current financial position is weak. This condition is partly reflected in Swofford's ability to make only one investment. More important, however, the firm's president believes that, if the next investment results in a substantial loss, Swofford's future will be in jeopardy. Although the expected value approach leads to a recommendation for d_1, do you think the firm's president would prefer this decision? We suspect that the president would select d_2 or d_3 to avoid the possibility of incurring a $50,000 loss. In fact, a reasonable conclusion is that, if a loss of even $30,000 could drive Swofford out of business, the president would select d_3, believing that both investments A and B are too risky for Swofford's current financial position.

The way we resolve Swofford's dilemma is first to determine Swofford's utility for the various monetary outcomes. Recall that the utility of any outcome is the total worth of that outcome, taking into account all risks and consequences involved. If the utilities for the various consequences are assessed correctly, the decision alternative with the highest expected utility is the most preferred, or best, alternative. In the next section we show how to determine the utility of the monetary outcomes so that the alternative with the highest expected utility can be identified.

5.2 UTILITY AND DECISION MAKING

The procedure we use to establish utility values for the payoffs in Swofford's situation requires that we first assign a utility value to the best and worst possible payoffs. Any values will work as long as the utility assigned to the best payoff is greater than the utility assigned

*Utility values of 0 and 1
could have been selected
here; we selected 0 and 10
in order to avoid any
possible confusion between
the utility value for a payoff
and the probability p.*

to the worst payoff. In this case, $50,000 is the best payoff and $-$50,000 is the worst. Suppose, then, that we arbitrarily make assignments to these two payoffs as follows:

$$\text{Utility of } -\$50,000 = U(-50,000) = 0$$
$$\text{Utility of } \quad \$50,000 = U(50,000) \quad = 10$$

Let us now determine the utility associated with every other payoff.

Consider the process of establishing the utility of a payoff of $30,000. First we ask Swofford's president to state a preference between a guaranteed $30,000 payoff and an opportunity to engage in the following **lottery,** or bet:

Lottery: Swofford obtains a payoff of $50,000 with probability p
and a payoff of $-$50,000 with probability $(1 - p)$.

*p is often referred to as the
indifference probability.*

Obviously, if p is very close to 1, Swofford's president would prefer the lottery to the guaranteed payoff of $30,000 because the firm would virtually ensure itself a payoff of $50,000. If p is very close to 0, Swofford's president would clearly prefer the guarantee of $30,000. In any event, as p changes continuously from 0 to 1, the preference for the guaranteed payoff of $30,000 will change at some point into a preference for the lottery. At this value of p, Swofford's president would have no greater preference for the guaranteed payoff of $30,000 than for the lottery. For example, let us assume that when $p = 0.95$, Swofford's president is indifferent between the guaranteed payoff of $30,000 and the lottery. For this value of p, we can compute the utility of a $30,000 payoff as follows:

$$U(30,000) = pU(50,000) + (1 - p)U(-50,000)$$
$$= 0.95(10) + (0.05)(0)$$
$$= 9.5$$

Obviously, if we had started with a different assignment of utilities for a payoff of $50,000 and $-$50,000, the result would have been a different utility for $30,000. For example, if we had started with an assignment of 100 for $50,000 and 10 for $-$50,000, the utility of a $30,000 payoff would be

$$U(30,000) = 0.95(100) + 0.05(10)$$
$$= 95 + 0.5$$
$$= 95.5$$

Hence, we must conclude that the utility assigned to each payoff is not unique but merely depends on the initial choice of utilities for the best and worst payoffs. We will discuss utility choice further at the end of the section. For now, however, we will continue to use a value of 10 for the utility of $50,000 and a value of 0 for the utility of $-$50,000.

Before computing the utility for the other payoffs, let us consider the significance of Swofford's president assigning a utility of 9.5 to a payoff of $30,000. Clearly, when $p = 0.95$, the expected value of the lottery is

$$EV(\text{lottery}) = 0.95(\$50,000) + 0.05(-\$50,000)$$
$$= \$47,500 - \$2,500$$
$$= \$45,000$$

Although the expected value of the lottery when $p = 0.95$ is $45,000, Swofford's president would just as soon take a guaranteed payoff of $30,000. Thus, Swofford's president is taking a conservative, or risk-avoiding, viewpoint. A decision maker who would choose a guaranteed payoff over a lottery with a better expected payoff is a **risk avoider.** The president would rather have $30,000 for certain than risk anything greater than a 5% chance of incurring a loss of $50,000. In other words the difference between the EV of $45,000 and the guaranteed payoff of $30,000 is the risk premium that Swofford's president would be willing to pay to avoid the 5% chance of losing $50,000.

To compute the utility associated with a payoff of −$20,000, we must ask Swofford's president to state a preference between a guaranteed −$20,000 payoff and an opportunity to engage again in the following lottery:

> Lottery: Swofford obtains a payoff of $50,000 with probability p
> and a payoff of −$50,000 with probability $(1 − p)$

Note that this lottery is exactly the same as the one we used to establish the utility of a payoff of $30,000. In fact, we use this lottery to establish the utility for any monetary value in the Swofford payoff table. We need to determine the value of p that would make the president indifferent between a guaranteed payoff of −$20,000 and the lottery. For example, we might begin by asking the president to choose between a certain loss of $20,000 and the lottery with a payoff of $50,000 with probability $p = 0.90$ and a payoff of −$50,000 with probability $(1 − p) = 0.10$. What answer do you think we would get? Surely, with this high probability of obtaining a payoff of $50,000, the president would elect the lottery. Next, we might ask whether $p = 0.85$ would result in indifference between the loss of $20,000 for certain and the lottery. Again the president might prefer the lottery. Suppose that we continue until we get to $p = 0.55$, at which point the president is indifferent between the payoff of −$20,000 and the lottery. That is, for any value of p less than 0.55, the president would take a loss of $20,000 for certain rather than risk the potential loss of $50,000 with the lottery; and for any value of p above 0.55, the president would choose the lottery. Thus, the utility assigned to a payoff of −$20,000 is

$$U(-\$20,000) = pU(50,000) + (1 − p)U(-\$50,000)$$
$$= 0.55(10) + 0.45(0)$$
$$= 5.5$$

Again let us compare the significance of this assignment to the expected value approach. When $p = 0.55$, the expected value of the lottery is

$$EV(\text{lottery}) = 0.55(\$50,000) + 0.45(-\$50,000)$$
$$= \$27,500 − \$22,500$$
$$= \$5,000$$

Thus, Swofford's president would just as soon absorb a loss of $20,000 for certain as take the lottery, even though the expected value of the lottery is $5000. Once again this preference demonstrates the conservative, or risk-avoiding, point of view of Swofford's president.

In these two examples we computed the utility for the monetary payoffs of $30,000 and −$20,000. We can determine the utility for any monetary payoff M in a similar fashion. First, we must find the probability p for which the decision maker is indifferent between a guaranteed payoff of M and a lottery with a payoff of $50,000 with probability p and −$50,000 with probability $(1 − p)$. The utility of M is then computed as follows:

$$U(M) = pU(\$50,000) + (1 − p)U(-\$50,000)$$
$$= p(10) + (1 − p)0$$
$$= 10p$$

TABLE 5.2   UTILITY OF MONETARY PAYOFFS FOR SWOFFORD, INC.

Monetary Value	Indifference Value of p	Utility Value
$ 50,000	Does not apply	10.0
30,000	0.95	9.5
20,000	0.90	9.0
0	0.75	7.5
−20,000	0.55	5.5
−30,000	0.40	4.0
−50,000	Does not apply	0

Using this procedure we developed utility values for the rest of the payoffs in Swofford's problem. The results are presented in Table 5.2.

Now that we have determined the utility value of each of the possible monetary values, we can write the original payoff table in terms of utility values. Table 5.3 shows the utility for the various outcomes in the Swofford problem. The notation we use for the entries in the utility table is U_{ij}, which denotes the utility associated with decision alternative d_i and state of nature s_j. Using this notation, we see that $U_{23} = 4.0$.

The Expected Utility Approach

We can now apply the expected value computations introduced in Chapter 4 to the utilities in Table 5.3 in order to select an optimal decision alternative for Swofford, Inc. However, because utility values represent such a special case of expected value, we will refer to the expected value when applied to utility values as the **expected utility (EU).** Thus, the expected utility approach requires the analyst to compute the expected utility for each decision alternative and then select the alternative yielding the highest expected utility. With N possible states of nature, the expected utility of a decision alternative d_i is given by

$$EU(d_i) = \sum_{j=1}^{N} P(s_j)U_{ij} \qquad (5.1)$$

The expected utility for each of the decision alternatives in the Swofford problem is

$$EU(d_1) = 0.3(9.5) + 0.5(9.0) + 0.2(0) \quad = 7.35$$
$$EU(d_2) = 0.3(10) \ + 0.5(5.5) + 0.2(4.0) = 6.55$$
$$EU(d_3) = 0.3(7.5) + 0.5(7.5) + 0.2(7.5) = 7.50$$

TABLE 5.3   UTILITY TABLE FOR SWOFFORD, INC.

| Decision Alternative | State of Nature | | |
	Prices Up s_1	Prices Stable s_2	Prices Down s_3
Investment A, d_1	9.5	9.0	0
Investment B, d_2	10.0	5.5	4.0
Do not invest, d_3	7.5	7.5	7.5

Can you use the expected utility approach to determine the optimal decision? Try Problem 1.

Note that the optimal decision using the expected utility approach is d_3, do not invest. The ranking of alternatives according to the president's utility assignments and the associated monetary values are as follows.

Ranking of Decision Alternatives	Expected Utility	Expected Monetary Value
Do not invest	7.50	0
Investment A	7.35	9000
Investment B	6.55	−1000

Note that although investment A had the highest expected monetary value of $9000, the analysis indicates that Swofford should decline this investment. The rationale behind not selecting investment A is that the 0.20 probability of a $50,000 loss was considered to involve a serious risk by Swofford's president. The seriousness of this risk and its associated impact on the company were not adequately reflected by the expected monetary value of investment A. We assessed the utility for each payoff to assess this risk adequately.

NOTES AND COMMENTS

In the Swofford problem we have been using a utility of 10 for the best payoff and 0 for the worst. The choice of values could have been anything, and we might have chosen 1 for the utility of the best payoff and 0 for the utility of the worst. Had we made this choice, the utility for any monetary value M would have been the value of p at which the decision maker was indifferent between a guaranteed payoff of M and a lottery in which the best payoff is obtained with probability p and the worst payoff is obtained with probability $(1 - p)$. Thus, the utility for any monetary value would have been equal to the probability of earning the best payoff. Often this choice is made because of the ease in computation. We chose not to do so to emphasize the distinction between the utility values and the indifference probabilities for the lottery.

Summary of Steps for Determining the Utility of Money

Before considering other aspects of utility, let us summarize the steps involved in determining the utility for a monetary value and using it within the decision analysis framework. The following steps state in general terms the procedure used to solve the Swofford, Inc., investment problem.

Step 1. Develop a payoff table using monetary values.
Step 2. Identify the best and worst payoff values in the table and assign each a utility value, with U(best payoff) > U(worst payoff).
Step 3. For every other monetary value M in the original payoff table, do the following to determine its utility value.
   a. Define the lottery: The best payoff is obtained with probability p and the worst payoff is obtained with probability $(1 - p)$.
   b. Determine the value of p such that the decision maker is indifferent between a guaranteed payoff of M and the lottery defined in step 3(a).
   c. Calculate the utility of M as follows:

   $$U(M) = pU(\text{best payoff}) + (1 - p)U(\text{worst payoff})$$

Step 4. Convert the payoff table from monetary values to utility values.
Step 5. Apply the expected utility approach to the utility table developed in step 4 and select the decision alternative with the highest expected utility.

NOTES AND COMMENTS

The procedure we described for determining the utility of monetary consequences can also be used to develop a utility measure for nonmonetary consequences. Assign the best consequence a utility of 10 and the worst a utility of 0. Then create a lottery with a probability of p for the best consequence and $(1 - p)$ for the worst consequence. For each of the other consequences, find the value of p that makes the decision maker indifferent between the lottery and the consequence. Then calculate the utility of the consequence in question as follows:

$$U(\text{consequence}) = pU(\text{best consequence}) + (1 - p)U(\text{worst consequence})$$

5.3   UTILITY: OTHER CONSIDERATIONS

In this section, we describe how a risk-avoiding decision maker and a risk-taking decision maker differ in their assessment of utility. Expected utility is then used to show how a risk-avoiding decision maker and a risk-taking decision maker may prefer different decision alternatives for the same decision problem. We close this section by comparing expected monetary value and expected utility as criteria for decision making.

Risk Avoiders Versus Risk Takers

The financial position of Swofford, Inc., was such that the firm's president evaluated investment opportunities from a conservative, or risk-avoiding, point of view. However, if the firm had a surplus of cash and a stable future, Swofford's president might have been looking for investment alternatives that, although perhaps risky, contained a potential for substantial profit. That type of behavior would have made the president a risk taker.

A **risk taker** is a decision maker who would choose a lottery over a better guaranteed payoff. In this section we analyze the decision problem faced by Swofford from the point of view of a decision maker who would be classified as a risk taker. We then compare the conservative, or risk-avoiding, point of view of Swofford's president with the behavior of a decision maker who is a risk taker.

For the decision problem facing Swofford, Inc., and using the general procedure for developing utilities as discussed in Section 5.2, a risk taker might express the utility for the various payoffs shown in Table 5.4. As before, $U(50,000) = 10$ and $U(-50,000) = 0$. Note the difference in behavior reflected in Table 5.4 and Table 5.2. That is, in determining the value of p at which the decision maker is indifferent between a guaranteed payoff of M and a lottery in which $50,000 is obtained with probability p and $-\$50,000$ with

TABLE 5.4   REVISED UTILITY VALUES FOR SWOFFORD, INC., ASSUMING A RISK TAKER

Monetary Value	Indifference Value of p	Utility Value
$ 50,000	Does not apply	10.0
30,000	0.50	5.0
20,000	0.40	4.0
0	0.25	2.5
−20,000	0.15	1.5
−30,000	0.10	1.0
−50,000	Does not apply	0

TABLE 5.5 PAYOFF TABLE FOR SWOFFORD, INC.

	State of Nature		
Decision Alternative	Prices Up s_1	Prices Stable s_2	Prices Down s_3
Investment A, d_1	$30,000	$20,000	−$50,000
Investment B, d_2	$50,000	−$20,000	−$30,000
Do not invest, d_3	0	0	0

probability $(1 - p)$, the risk taker is willing to accept a greater risk of incurring a loss of $50,000 in order to gain the opportunity to realize a profit of $50,000.

To help develop the utility table for the risk taker, we have reproduced the Swofford, Inc., payoff table in Table 5.5. Using these payoffs and the risk taker's utility values given in Table 5.4, we can write the risk taker's utility table as shown in Table 5.6. Using the state-of-nature probabilities $P(s_1) = 0.3$, $P(s_2) = 0.5$, and $P(s_3) = 0.2$, the expected utility for each decision alternative is

$$EU(d_1) = 0.3(5.0) + 0.5(4.0) + 0.2(0) = 3.50$$
$$EU(d_2) = 0.3(10) + 0.5(1.5) + 0.2(1.0) = 3.95$$
$$EU(d_3) = 0.3(2.5) + 0.5(2.5) + 0.2(2.5) = 2.50$$

What is the recommended decision? Perhaps somewhat to your surprise, the analysis recommends investment B, with the highest expected utility of 3.95. Recall that this investment has a −$1000 expected monetary value. Why is it now the recommended decision? Remember that the decision maker in this revised problem is a risk taker. Thus, although the expected value of investment B is negative, utility analysis has shown that this decision maker is enough of a risk taker to prefer investment B and its potential for the $50,000 profit.

The expected utility values give the following order of preference of the decision alternatives for the risk taker and the associated expected monetary values.

Ranking of Decision Alternatives	Expected Utility	Expected Monetary Value
Investment B	3.95	−$1000
Investment A	3.50	$9000
Do not invest	2.50	0

TABLE 5.6 UTILITY TABLE OF A RISK TAKER FOR SWOFFORD, INC.

	State of Nature		
Decision Alternative	Prices Up s_1	Prices Stable s_2	Prices Down s_3
Investment A, d_1	5.0	4.0	0
Investment B, d_2	10.0	1.5	1.0
Do not invest, d_3	2.5	2.5	2.5

Comparing the utility analysis for a risk taker with the more conservative preferences of the president of Swofford, Inc., who is a risk avoider, we see that, even with the same decision problem, different attitudes toward risk can lead to different recommended decisions. The utility values established by Swofford's president indicated that the firm should not invest at this time, whereas the utilities established by the risk taker showed a preference for investment B. Note that both of these decisions differ from the best expected monetary value decision, which was investment A.

We can obtain another perspective of the difference between behaviors of a risk avoider and a risk taker by developing a graph that depicts the relationship between monetary value and utility. We use the horizontal axis of the graph to represent monetary values and the vertical axis to represent the utility associated with each monetary value. Now, consider the data in Table 5.2, with a utility value corresponding to each monetary value for the original Swofford, Inc., problem. These values can be plotted on a graph such as that in Figure 5.1, and a curve can be drawn through the observed points. The resulting curve is the **utility function for money** for Swofford's president. Recall that these points reflected the conservative, or risk-avoiding, nature of Swofford's president. Hence, we refer to the curve in Figure 5.1 as a utility function for a risk avoider. Using the data in Table 5.4, developed for a risk taker, we can plot these points on a graph such as that in Figure 5.2. The resulting curve depicts the utility function for a risk taker.

By looking at the utility functions of Figures 5.1 and 5.2, we can begin to generalize about the utility functions for risk avoiders and risk takers. Although the exact shape of the utility function will vary from one decision maker to another, we can see the general shape of these two types of utility functions. The utility function for a risk avoider shows a diminishing marginal return for money. For example, the increase in utility going from a monetary value of −$30,000 to $0 is 7.5 − 4.0 = 3.5, whereas the increase in utility in going from $0 to $30,000 is only 9.5 − 7.5 = 2.0. However, the utility function for a risk taker shows an increasing marginal return for money. For example, in Figure 5.2, the increase in utility in going from −$30,000 to $0 is 2.5 − 1.0 = 1.5, whereas the increase in utility in going from $0 to $30,000

FIGURE 5.1   UTILITY FUNCTION FOR MONEY FOR THE RISK AVOIDER

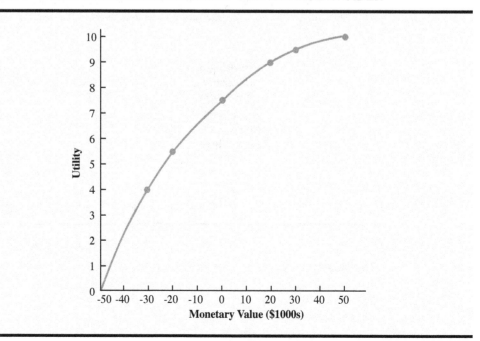

FIGURE 5.2   UTILITY FUNCTION FOR MONEY FOR THE RISK TAKER

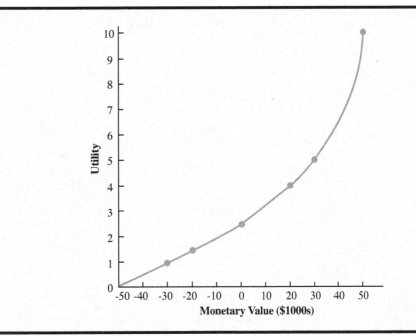

is $5.0 - 2.5 = 2.5$. Note also that in either case the utility function is always increasing; that is, more money leads to more utility. All utility functions possess this property.

We concluded that the utility function for a risk avoider shows a diminishing marginal return for money and that the utility function for a risk taker shows an increasing marginal return. When the marginal return for money is neither decreasing nor increasing but remains constant, the corresponding utility function describes the behavior of a decision maker who is neutral to risk. The following characteristics are associated with a **risk-neutral decision maker.**

1. The utility function can be drawn as a straight line connecting the "best" and the "worst" points.
2. The expected utility approach and the expected value approach applied to monetary payoffs result in the same action.

Try Problem 5 for practice in plotting the utility function for risk-avoider, risk-taker, and risk-neutral decision makers.

Figure 5.3 depicts the utility function of a risk-neutral decision maker using the Swofford, Inc., problem data. For comparison purposes, we also show the utility functions for the cases where the decision maker is either a risk taker or a risk avoider.

Expected Monetary Value Versus Expected Utility

In many decision-making problems, expected monetary value and expected utility will lead to identical recommendations. In fact, this result will always be true if the decision maker is risk neutral. In general, if the decision maker is almost risk neutral over the range of payoffs (from lowest to highest) for a particular decision problem, the decision alternative with the best expected monetary value leads to selection of the most preferred decision alternative. The trick lies in recognizing the range of monetary values over which a decision maker's utility function is risk neutral.

Generally, when the payoffs for a particular decision-making problem fall into a reasonable range—the best is not too good and the worst is not too bad—decision makers tend to express preferences in agreement with the expected monetary value approach. Thus, we

FIGURE 5.3   UTILITY FUNCTIONS FOR RISK-AVOIDER, RISK-TAKER, AND
RISK-NEUTRAL DECISION MAKERS

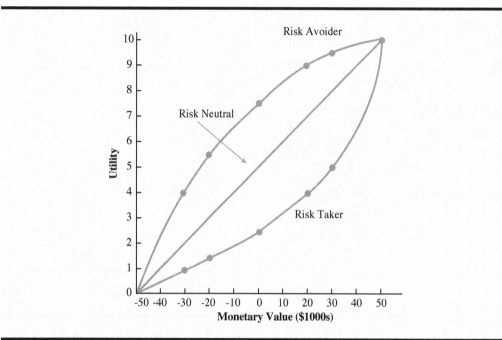

suggest asking the decision maker to consider the best and worst possible payoffs for a problem and assess their reasonableness. If the decision maker believes that they are in the reasonable range, the decision alternative with the best expected monetary value can be used. However, if the payoffs appear unreasonably large or unreasonably small (for example, a huge loss) and if the decision maker believes that monetary values do not adequately reflect her or his true preferences for the payoffs, a utility analysis of the problem should be considered.

Unfortunately, determination of the appropriate utilities is not a trivial task. As we have shown, measuring utility requires a degree of subjectivity on the part of the decision maker, and different decision makers will have different utility functions. This aspect of utility often causes decision makers to feel uncomfortable about using the expected utility approach. However, if you encounter a decision situation in which you are convinced that monetary value is not the sole measure of performance, and if you agree that a quantitative analysis of the decision problem is desirable, you should recommend that utility analysis be considered.

5.4   INTRODUCTION TO GAME THEORY

Until 1944, when Von Neumann and Morgenstern published the book Theory of Games and Economic Behavior, *the literature on decisions involving risk consisted primarily of applications involving the use of probability in gambling.*

In decision analysis, a single decision maker seeks to select an optimal decision alternative after considering the possible outcomes of one or more chance events. In **game theory,** two or more decision makers are called players, and they compete as adversaries against each other. Each player selects a strategy independently without knowing in advance the strategy of the other player or players. The combination of the competing strategies provides the value of the game to the players. Game theory applications have been developed for situations in which the competing players are teams, companies, political candidates, armies, and contract bidders.

In this section, we describe **two-person, zero-sum games.** *Two-person* means that two competing players take part in the game. *Zero-sum* means that the gain (or loss) for one player is equal to the corresponding loss (gain) for the other player. As a result, the gain and loss balance out so that the game results in the sum of zero. What one player wins, the other player loses. Let us demonstrate a two-person, zero-sum game and its solution by considering two companies competing for market share.

Competing for Market Share

Suppose that two companies are the only manufacturers of a particular product; they compete against each other for market share. In planning a marketing strategy for the coming year, each company is considering three strategies designed to take market share from the other company. The three strategies, assumed to be the same for both companies, are as follows:

Strategy 1   Increase advertising
Strategy 2   Provide quantity discounts
Strategy 3   Extend product warranty

A payoff table showing the percentage gain in the market share for Company A expected for each combination of strategies follows. The notations a_1, a_2, and a_3 identify the three strategies for Company A; the notations b_1, b_2, and b_3 identify the three strategies for Company B. It is a zero-sum game because any gain in market share for Company A is a loss in market share for Company B.

		Company B		
		Increase Advertising b_1	Quantity Discounts b_2	Extend Warranty b_3
Company A	Increase Advertising, a_1	4	3	2
	Quantity Discounts, a_2	−1	4	1
	Extend Warranty, a_3	5	−2	0

In interpreting the entries in the table we see that if Company A increases advertising (a_1) and Company B increases advertising (b_1), Company A will come out ahead with an increase in market share of 4%. On the other hand, if Company A provides quantity discounts (a_2) and Company B increases advertising (b_1), Company A is projected to lose 1% of market share to Company B. Company A is seeking payoff values that show relatively large increases in its market share. Company B is seeking payoff values that show decreases or small increases in Company A's market share, and thus better results for Company B.

This game involving market share meets the requirements of a two-person, zero-sum game. The two companies are the two players and the zero-sum occurs because the gain in market share for Company A is the same as the loss in market share for Company B. Due to the planning horizon, each company must select a strategy before knowing the other company's strategy. What are the optimal strategies for the two companies?

The logic of game theory assumes that each company or player has the same information and will select a strategy that provides the best possible outcome from its point of view. Suppose Company A selects strategy a_1. Market share increases of 4%, 3%, or 2% are possible depending upon Company B's strategy. If Company B believes that Company A will use strategy a_1, then Company B will employ strategy b_3. Under the assumption that Company B will select the strategy that is best for it, Company A analyzes the game by protecting itself against the actions of Company B. In doing so, Company A identifies the minimum possible payoff for each of its actions. This payoff is the minimum value in each row of the payoff matrix. These row minimums are computed in the payoff table as follows:

	Company B			
	Increase Advertising b_1	Quantity Discounts b_2	Extend Warranty b_3	Minimum
Increase Advertising, a_1	4	3	2	②
Quantity Discounts, a_2	-1	4	1	-1
Extend Warranty, a_3	5	-2	0	-2

Company A (label at left of rows)

Maximum of
row minimums

Considering the entries in the Minimum column, we see that Company A can be guaranteed an increase in market share of at least 2 percent by selecting the strategy that provides the *maximum of the row minimums* (strategy a_1). Thus, Company A follows a *maximin* procedure and selects strategy a_1 as its best strategy.

Let us now look at the payoff table from the point of view of the other player, Company B. The entries in the payoff table represent losses in market share. Consider what happens to Company B if strategy b_1 is selected. Market share decreases of 4%, –1%, and 5% are possible. Under the assumption that Company A will select the strategy that is best for it, Company B knows that if it selects strategy b_1, a loss in market share of as much as 5% could be incurred. Thus, Company B analyzes the game by considering the maximum value in each column, which provides the maximum decrease in its market share for each Company A strategy. These column maximums are computed as follows:

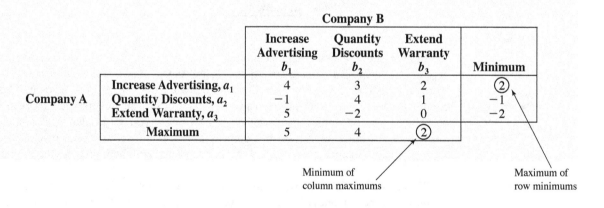

	Company B			
	Increase Advertising b_1	Quantity Discounts b_2	Extend Warranty b_3	Minimum
Increase Advertising, a_1	4	3	2	②
Quantity Discounts, a_2	-1	4	1	-1
Extend Warranty, a_3	5	-2	0	-2
Maximum	5	4	②	

Minimum of
column maximums

Maximum of
row minimums

By considering the entries in the Maximum row, Company B can be guaranteed a decrease in market share of no more than 2% by selecting the strategy that provides the *minimum of the column maximums* (strategy b_3). Thus, Company B follows a *minimax* procedure and selects strategy b_3 as its best strategy. Under strategy b_3 Company B knows that Company A cannot gain more than 2% in market share.

Identifying a Pure Strategy

Whenever, the maximum of the row minimums *equals* the minimum of the column maximums, the players cannot improve their outcomes by changing strategies. The game is said to have a **saddle point.** With a saddle point, the optimal strategies and the value of the game cannot be improved by either player changing strategies. Thus, a **pure strategy** has been identified as being optimal for both players. The requirement for a pure strategy is as follows:

$$\text{Maximum(Row minimums)} = \text{Minimum(Column maximums)}$$

That is, the maximin value for Player A equals the minimax value for Player B. In this example, the solution to the game is for Company A to increase its advertising (strategy a_1) and Company B to extend its product warranty (strategy b_3). The value of the game shows that this optimal solution will increase Company A's market share by 2% and decrease Company B's market share by 2%.

With a pure strategy, neither player can improve its position by changing to a different strategy. In our marketing example, the pure strategy for Company A is a_1. When Company B selects its pure strategy b_3 the value of the game shows an increase in Company A's market share of 2%. Note that if Company B tries to change its pure strategy from b_3, Company A's market share will increase 4% if b_1 is selected or will increase 3% if b_2 is selected. Company B must stay with its pure strategy b_3 to obtain its best result. Similarly note that if Company A tries to change its pure strategy from a_1, Company A's market share will increase only 1% if a_2 is selected or will not increase at all if a_3 is selected. Company A must stay with its pure strategy a_1 in order to keep its 2% increase in market share. Thus, even if one of the players discovered in advance the opponent's strategy, no advantage could be gained by switching to a different strategy.

If a pure strategy exists, it is the optimal solution for the game.

When a pure strategy is optimal for a two-person, zero-sum game the following steps will find the optimal strategy for each player.

Step 1. Compute the minimum payoff for each row (Player A).
Step 2. For Player A, select the strategy that provides the *maximum* of the row minimums.
Step 3. Compute the maximum payoff for each column (Player B).
Step 4. For Player B select the strategy that provides the *minimum* of the column maximums.
Step 5. If the maximin value (step 2) equals the minimax value (step 4), an optimal pure strategy exists for both players. The optimal strategy for Player A is identified in step 2, and the optimal strategy for Player B is identified in step 4. The value of the game is given by the value at the saddle point where the optimal strategies for both players intersect.

If in step 5 the maximin value for Player A does not equal the minimax value for Player B, a pure strategy is not optimal for the two-person, zero-sum game. In this case, a *mixed strategy* is best. We show when it is necessary to employ a mixed strategy in the next section.

5.5   MIXED STRATEGY GAMES

Consider the two-person, zero-sum game that occurs in a football game. The two competing players are the two football teams. On each play, the game is zero-sum because the yardage gained by one team is equal to the yardage lost by the other team. As usual in game theory, each team must select its strategy before knowing the strategy selected by the other team. In this example, let Team A be the team on offense trying to gain yardage and Team B be the team on defense trying to keep the yardage gained by Team A to a minimum. We define the offensive strategies for Team A as follows:

$$a_1 = \text{running play}$$
$$a_2 = \text{passing play}$$

The defensive strategies for Team B are as follows:

$$b_1 = \text{run defense}$$
$$b_2 = \text{pass defense}$$

The payoff table shows the yardage gained by Team A depending upon the strategies selected by the two teams.

		Team B	
		Run defense b_1	Pass defense b_2
Team A	Run, a_1	1	6
	Pass, a_2	15	0

Applying the five-step procedure used to identify a pure strategy, the row minimums and the column maximums are as follows:

		Team B		
		Run defense b_1	Pass defense b_2	Minimum
Team A	Run, a_1	1	6	①
	Pass, a_2	15	0	0
	Maximum	15	⑥	

The maximum of the row minimums is 1 and the minimum of the column maximums is 6. Because these values are not equal, the two-person, zero-sum game does not have an optimal pure strategy. In this case, a **mixed strategy** solution is best. With a mixed strategy, the optimal solution for each player is to randomly select among the alternative strategies. In the football example, then, the offensive Team A will mix up or vary its selection of running (a_1) and passing (a_2) plays, while the defensive Team B will mix up or vary its selection of a run defense (b_1) and a pass defense (b_2).

When you think about a football game, it becomes clear that a pure strategy such as Team A always selecting a running play would not work. Team B would recognize Team A's pure strategy and would always be prepared with a run defense. Thus, a Team A mixed strategy of sometimes running and sometimes passing would make sense. When a mixed strategy solution is needed, game theory will determine the optimal probabilities for each strategy for each player. That is, the game theory solution of the football example will tell the offensive team the optimal probabilities for a running play and a passing play. At the same time, the solution will tell the defensive team the optimal probabilities for a run defense and a pass defense. The following discussion shows how to calculate these mixed strategy probabilities.

Let

$$p = \text{the probability Team A selects a running play}$$
$$(1 - p) = \text{the probability Team A selects a passing play}$$

When a mixed strategy solution exists, we seek to determine the probability p for Team A such that Team B cannot improve its result by changing its defensive strategy. First assume that Team B selects a run defense as shown in column b_1. If Team A selects a running play with probability p and a passing play with probability $(1 - p)$, the expected value of the yardage gain for Team A is computed as follows:

If Team B selects b_1:

$$EV(Yardage) = 1p + 15(1 - p)$$

If Team B selects its pass defense as shown in column b_2, the expected value of the yardage gain for Team A will be as follows:

If Team B selects b_2:

$$EV(Yardage) = 6p + 0(1 - p) = 6p$$

To guarantee that Team B cannot change its strategy and decrease the expected value of the yardage gained by Team A, we set the two expected values equal and solve for the value of p.

$$1p + 15(1 - p) = 6p$$
$$1p + 15 - 15p = 6p$$
$$20p = 15$$
$$p = 15/20 = .75$$

With $p = .75, (1 - p) = 1 - .75 = .25$. This result tells Team A it should select a running play with a .75 probably and a passing play with a .25 probability. The expected value of the yardage gained, which is the *value of the game,* is

$$EV(Yardage) = 1p + 15(1 - p) = 1(.75) + 15(.25) = 4.5 \text{ yards per play}$$

Now let us consider the optimal probabilities for Team B. Let

$$q = \text{the probability Team B selects a run defense}$$
$$(1 - q) = \text{the probability Team B selects a pass defense}$$

Using the same logic we used for computing Team A's optimal probabilities, we want to determine the value of q such that Team A cannot increase the expected value of the yardage gained by changing its offensive strategy. We first compute the expected value of the yardage for Team B for the following two cases:

If Team A selects a_1:

$$EV(Yardage) = 1q + 6(1 - q)$$

If Team A selects a_2:

$$EV(Yardage) = 15q + 0(1 - q) = 15q$$

To guarantee that Team A cannot change its strategy and affect the expected value of the yardage for Team B, we set the two expected values equal and solve for the value of q as follows:

$$1q + 6(1 - q) = 15q$$
$$1q + 6 - 6q = 15q$$
$$20q = 6$$
$$q = 6/20 = .30$$

With $q = .30, (1 - q) = 1 - .30 = .70$. This result tells Team B that it should select a run defense with a .30 probably and a pass defense with a .70 probability. The expected yardage gained, which is the value of the game, will remain 4.5 yards per play.

Thus, we have the optimal mixed strategy solution for the football game example. Any 2×2 two-person, zero-sum mixed strategy game can be solved algebraically as shown in this example. If a larger two-person, zero-sum game involves a mixed strategy, solving it is a bit more complicated.

A Larger Mixed Strategy Game

Consider the following two-person, zero-sum game.

		Player B		
		b_1	b_2	b_3
	a_1	0	-1	2
Player A	a_2	5	4	-3
	a_3	2	3	-4

Following the usual procedure for identifying a pure strategy, we compute the row minimums and the column maximums.

		Player B			
		b_1	b_2	b_3	**Minimum**
	a_1	0	-1	2	(−1)
Player A	a_2	5	4	-3	-3
	a_3	2	3	-4	-4
Maximum		5	4	(2)	

The maximum of the row minimums is -1 and the minimum of the column maximums is 2. Because the maximin and minimax values are not equal, the two-person, zero-sum game does not have an optimal pure strategy. However, with a problem larger than 2×2, we cannot use the algebraic solution for the mixed strategy probabilities as we did in the previous example.

If a game larger than 2×2 requires a mixed strategy, we first look for dominated strategies in order to reduce the size of the game. A **dominated strategy** exists if another strategy *is at least as good* regardless of what the opponent does. For example, consider strategies a_2 and a_3. The payoff table shows that in column b_1, $5 > 2$, in column b_2, $4 > 3$, and in column b_3, $-3 > -4$. Thus, regardless of what Player B does, Player A will always prefer the higher values of strategy a_2 compared to strategy a_3. Thus, strategy a_3 is dominated by strategy a_2 and thus strategy a_3 can be dropped from consideration by Player A. Eliminating dominated strategies from the game reduces its size. After eliminating a_3, the reduced game becomes

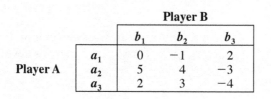

		Player B		
		b_1	b_2	b_3
Player A	a_1	0	-1	2
	a_2	5	4	-3

Next we look for more dominated strategies. Player A finds no other dominated strategies. However, consider strategies b_1 and b_2 for Player B. Remember that Player B is interested in smaller values. The payoff table shows that in row a_1, $-1 < 0$ and in row a_2, $4 < 5$. Thus, regardless of what Player A does, Player B would always prefer the smaller values of strategy b_2 compared to strategy b_1. Thus, strategy b_1 is dominated by strategy b_2 and can be eliminated from the game. With this dominated strategy eliminated, the reduced game becomes

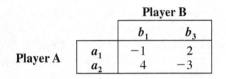

Problem 14 at the end of the chapter will ask you to find the optimal probabilities for this example.

By successively eliminating dominated strategies, we reduce the game to a 2×2 game. The algebraic solution procedure described earlier in this section can now be used to identify the optimal probabilities for the mixed strategy solution.

Finally, it is important to realize that no hard-and-fast rule identifies dominated strategies. Basically, the analyst must make pairwise comparisons of the decision strategies in an attempt to identify dominated strategies. The goal is to identify and eliminate dominated strategies sequentially in order to reduce the game to a 2×2 game so that an algebraic solution procedure can be used to solve for the mixed strategy probabilities.

Identifying and eliminating dominated strategies may reduce the game to a 2×2 game. If so, an algebraic procedure may be used to determine the mixed strategy solution.

Summary of Steps for Solving Two-Person, Zero-Sum Games

The following summary shows the steps used to solve two-person, zero-sum games.

1. Use the maximin procedure for Player A and the minimax procedure for Player B to determine whether a pure strategy solution exists. (See previous steps for identifying a pure strategy.) If a pure strategy exists, it is the optimal solution.
2. If a pure strategy does not exist and the game is larger than 2×2, identify a dominated strategy to eliminate a row or column. Develop the reduced payoff table and continue to use dominance to eliminate as many additional rows and columns as possible.
3. If the reduced game is 2×2, solve for the optimal mixed strategy probabilities algebraically.

If the game cannot be reduced to a 2×2 game, a linear programming model can be used to solve for the optimal mixed strategy probabilities. The formulation of a linear programming model to solve these larger game theory problems is beyond the scope of this text.

Extensions

In 1994, John Harsanui, John Nash, and Reinhard Selten received the Nobel Prize in Economics for their work on noncooperative game theory.

We presented the basic model for two-person, zero-sum games. However, game theory models extend beyond two-person, zero-sum games. One extension is a two-person, constant-sum game that occurs when the payoffs for the strategies chosen sum to a constant other than zero. In addition, game theory can be extended to include more general n-person games. Cooperative games where players are allowed preplay communications is another variation. Finally, some game theory models allow an infinite number of strategies to be available for the players.

SUMMARY

In this chapter we showed how utility could be used in decision-making situations in which monetary value did not provide an adequate measure of the payoffs. Utility is a measure of the total worth of a consequence. As such, utility takes into account the decision maker's assessment of all aspects of a consequence including profit, loss, risk, and perhaps additional nonmonetary factors. The examples showed how the use of expected utility can lead to decision recommendations that differ from those based on expected monetary value.

A decision maker's judgment must be used to establish the utility for each consequence. We presented a step-by-step procedure to determine a decision maker's utility for monetary payoffs. We also discussed how conservative, risk-avoiding decision makers assess utility differently from more aggressive, risk-taking decision makers. If the decision maker is risk neutral, we showed that the solution using expected utility is identical to the solution using expected monetary value.

We presented an introduction to game theory by describing how to solve two-person, zero-sum games. In these games, the two players end up with the sum of the gain (loss) to one player and the loss (gain) to the other player always equal to zero. We described the steps that can be used to determine whether a two-person, zero-sum game results in an optimal pure strategy. If a pure strategy is optimal, a saddle point determines the value of the game. If an optimal pure strategy does not exist for a two-person, zero-sum 2×2 game, we showed how to identify an optimal mixed strategy. With a mixed strategy, each player uses probability to select a strategy for each play of the game. We showed how dominance could be used to reduce the size of mixed strategy games. If the elimination of dominated strategies can reduce a larger game to a 2×2 game, an algebraic solution procedure can be used to find a solution. If the game cannot be reduced to a 2×2 game, a linear programming model is needed to determine the optimal mixed strategy solution.

GLOSSARY

Utility   A measure of the total worth of a consequence reflecting a decision maker's attitude toward considerations such as profit, loss, and risk.

Lottery   A hypothetical investment alternative with a probability p of obtaining the best payoff and a probability of $(1 - p)$ of obtaining the worst payoff.

Risk avoider   A decision maker who would choose a guaranteed payoff over a lottery with a better expected payoff.

Expected utility (EU)   The weighted average of the utilities associated with a decision alternative. The weights are the state-of-nature probabilities.

Risk taker   A decision maker who would choose a lottery over a better guaranteed payoff.

Utility function for money   A curve that depicts the relationship between monetary value and utility.

Risk-neutral decision maker   A decision maker who is neutral to risk. For this decision maker the decision alternative with the best expected monetary value is identical to the alternative with the highest expected utility.

Game theory   The study of decision situations in which two or more players compete as adversaries. The combination of strategies chosen by the players determines the value of the game to each player.

Two-person, zero-sum game   A game with two players in which the gain to one player is equal to the loss to the other player.

Saddle point   A condition that exists when pure strategies are optimal for both players in a two-person, zero-sum game. The saddle point occurs at the intersection of the optimal strategies for the players, and the value of the saddle point is the value of the game.

Pure strategy   A game solution that provides a single best strategy for each player.

Mixed strategy   A game solution in which the player randomly selects the strategy to play from among several strategies with positive probabilities. The solution to the mixed strategy game identifies the probabilities that each player should use to randomly select the strategy to play.

Dominated strategy   A strategy is dominated if another strategy is at least as good for every strategy that the opposing player may employ. A dominated strategy will never be selected by the player and as such, can be eliminated in order to reduce the size of the game.

PROBLEMS

1. A firm has three investment alternatives. Payoffs are in thousands of dollars.

	Economic Conditions		
Decision Alternative	Up s_1	Stable s_2	Down s_3
Investment A, d_1	100	25	0
Investment B, d_2	75	50	25
Investment C, d_3	50	50	50
Probabilities	0.40	0.30	0.30

a. Using the expected value approach, which decision is preferred?
b. For the lottery having a payoff of $100,000 with probability p and $0 with probability $(1 - p)$, two decision makers expressed the following indifference probabilities. Find the most preferred decision for each decision maker using the expected utility approach.

	Indifference Probability (p)	
Profit	Decision Maker A	Decision Maker B
$75,000	0.80	0.60
$50,000	0.60	0.30
$25,000	0.30	0.15

c. Why don't decision makers A and B select the same decision alternative?

2. Alexander Industries is considering purchasing an insurance policy for its new office building in St. Louis, Missouri. The policy has an annual cost of $10,000. If Alexander Industries doesn't purchase the insurance and minor fire damage occurs, a cost of $100,000 is anticipated; the cost if major or total destruction occurs is $200,000. The costs, including the state-of-nature probabilities, are as follows.

	Damage		
Decision Alternative	None s_1	Minor s_2	Major s_3
Purchase insurance, d_1	10,000	10,000	10,000
Do not purchase insurance, d_2	0	100,000	200,000
Probabilities	0.96	0.03	0.01

   a. Using the expected value approach, what decision do you recommend?

   b. What lottery would you use to assess utilities? (Note: Because the data are costs, the best payoff is $0.)

   c. Assume that you found the following indifference probabilities for the lottery defined in part (b). What decision would you recommend?

Cost	Indifference Probability
10,000	$p = 0.99$
100,000	$p = 0.60$

   d. Do you favor using expected value or expected utility for this decision problem? Why?

3. In a certain state lottery, a lottery ticket costs $2. In terms of the decision to purchase or not to purchase a lottery ticket, suppose that the following payoff table applies.

		State of Nature
Decision Alternatives	**Win s_1**	**Lose s_2**
Purchase lottery ticket, d_1	300,000	−2
Do not purchase lottery ticket, d_2	0	0

   a. A realistic estimate of the chances of winning are 1 in 250,000. Use the expected value approach to recommend a decision.

   b. If a particular decision maker assigns an indifference probability of 0.000001 to the $0 payoff, would this individual purchase a lottery ticket? Use expected utility to justify your answer.

4. Two different routes accommodate travel between two cities. Route A normally takes 60 minutes, and route B normally takes 45 minutes. If traffic problems are encountered on route A, the travel time increases to 70 minutes; traffic problems on route B increase travel time to 90 minutes. The probability of a delay is 0.20 for route A and 0.30 for route B.

   a. Using the expected value approach, what is the recommended route?

   b. If utilities are to be assigned to the travel times, what is the appropriate lottery? (Note: The smaller times should reflect higher utilities.)

   c. Use the lottery of part (b) and assume that the decision maker expresses indifference probabilities of

$$p = 0.80 \quad \text{for 60 minutes}$$
$$p = 0.60 \quad \text{for 70 minutes}$$

What route should this decision maker select? Is the decision maker a risk taker or a risk avoider?

5. Three decision makers have assessed utilities for the following decision problem (payoff in dollars).

		State of Nature	
Decision Alternative	s_1	s_2	s_3
d_1	20	50	−20
d_2	80	100	−100

The indifference probabilities are as follows.

	Indifference Probability (p)		
Payoff	**Decision Maker A**	**Decision Maker B**	**Decision Maker C**
100	1.00	1.00	1.00
80	0.95	0.70	0.90
50	0.90	0.60	0.75
20	0.70	0.45	0.60
−20	0.50	0.25	0.40
−100	0.00	0.00	0.00

    a. Plot the utility function for money for each decision maker.

    b. Classify each decision maker as a risk avoider, a risk taker, or risk neutral.

    c. For the payoff of 20, what is the premium that the risk avoider will pay to avoid risk? What is the premium that the risk taker will pay to have the opportunity of the high payoff?

6. In Problem 5, if $P(s_1) = 0.25$, $P(s_2) = 0.50$, and $P(s_3) = 0.25$, find a recommended decision for each of the three decision makers. (Note: For the same decision problem, different utilities can lead to different decisions.)

7. Suppose that the point spread for a particular sporting event is 10 points and that with this spread you are convinced you would have a 0.60 probability of winning a bet on your team. However, the local bookie will accept only a $1000 bet. Assuming that such bets are legal, would you bet on your team? (Disregard any commission charged by the bookie.) Remember that *you* must pay losses out of your own pocket. Your payoff table is as follows.

	State of Nature	
Decision Alternatives	**You Win**	**You Lose**
Bet	1000	−1000
Don't bet	0	0

    a. What decision does the expected value approach recommend?

    b. What is *your* indifference probability for the $0 payoff? (Although this choice isn't easy, be as realistic as possible. It is required for an analysis that reflects your attitude toward risk.)

    c. What decision would you make based on the expected utility approach? In this case are you a risk taker or risk avoider?

    d. Would other individuals assess the same utility values you do? Explain.

    e. If your decision in part (c) was to place the bet, repeat the analysis assuming a minimum bet of $10,000.

8. A Las Vegas roulette wheel has 38 different numerical values. If an individual bets on one number and wins, the payoff is 35 to 1.

    a. Show a payoff table for a $10 bet on one number for decision alternatives of bet and do not bet.

    b. What is the recommended decision using the expected value approach?

    c. Do the Las Vegas casinos want risk-taking or risk-avoiding customers? Explain.

    d. What range of utility values would a decision maker have to assign to the $0 payoff in order to have expected utility justify a decision to place the $10 bet?

9. A new product has the following profit projections and associated probabilities.

Profit	Probability
$150,000	0.10
$100,000	0.25
$ 50,000	0.20
0	0.15
−$ 50,000	0.20
−$100,000	0.10

    a. Use the expected value approach to decide whether to market the new product.

    b. Because of the high dollar values involved, especially the possibility of a $100,000 loss, the marketing vice president has expressed some concern about the use of the expected value approach. As a consequence, if a utility analysis is performed, what is the appropriate lottery?

    c. Assume that the following indifference probabilities are assigned. Do the utilities reflect the behavior of a risk taker or a risk avoider?

Profit	Indifference Probability (p)
$100,000	0.95
$ 50,000	0.70
0	0.50
−$ 50,000	0.25

    d. Use expected utility to make a recommended decision.

    e. Should the decision maker feel comfortable with the final decision recommended by the analysis?

10. A television network has been receiving low ratings for its programs. Currently, management is considering two alternatives for the Monday night 8:00 P.M.–9:00 P.M. time slot: a western with a well-known star, or a musical variety with a relatively unknown husband-and-wife team. The percentages of viewing audience estimates depend on the degree of program acceptance. The relevant data are as follows.

Program Acceptance	Percentage of Viewing Audience	
	Western	Musical Variety
High	30%	40%
Moderate	25%	20%
Poor	20%	15%

The probabilities associated with program acceptance levels are as follows.

Program Acceptance	Probability	
	Western	Musical Variety
High	0.30	0.30
Moderate	0.60	0.40
Poor	0.10	0.30

a. Using the expected value approach, which program should the network choose?
b. For a utility analysis, what is the appropriate lottery?
c. Based on the lottery in part (b), assume that the network's program manager has assigned the following indifference probabilities. Based on the use of utility measures, which program would you recommend? Is the manager a risk taker or a risk avoider?

Percentage of Audience	Indifference Probability (p)
30%	0.40
25%	0.30
20%	0.10

11. Consider the following two-person, zero-sum game. Identify the pure strategy. What is the value of the game?

		Player B		
		b_1	b_2	b_3
Player A	a_1	8	5	7
	a_2	2	4	10

12. Two television stations in a market compete with each other for viewing audience. Local programming options for the 5:00 P.M. weekday time slot include a sitcom rerun, an early news program, or a home improvement show. Assume that each station has the same three programming options and must make its preseason program selection before knowing what the other television station will do. The viewing audience changes in thousands of viewers for Station A are as follows.

		Station B		
		Sitcom	News	Home Improvement
		b_1	b_2	b_3
Station A	Sitcom, a_1	10	−5	3
	News, a_2	8	8	6
	Home Improvement, a_3	4	7	3

Determine the optimal programming strategy for each station. What is the value of the game?

13. Two Indiana state senate candidates must decide what city to visit the day before the November election. The same four cities, Indianapolis, Evansville, Fort Wayne, and South Bend are available for both candidates. These cities are listed as strategies 1 to 4 for each candidate. Travel plans must be made in advance, so the candidates must decide which city to visit prior to knowing the other candidate's plans. Values in the following table show thousands of voters for the Republican candidate based on the strategies selected by the two candidates. What city should each candidate visit, and what is the value of the game?

		Democrat Candidate			
		Indianapolis b_1	Evansville b_2	Fort Wayne b_3	South Bend b_4
Republican Candidate	Indianapolis, a_1	0	−15	−8	20
	Evansville, a_2	30	−5	5	−10
	Fort Wayne, a_3	10	−25	0	20
	South Bend, a_4	20	20	10	15

14. In Section 5.5, we showed the following two-person, zero-sum game had a mixed strategy.

		Player B		
		b_1	b_2	b_3
Player A	a_1	0	−1	2
	a_2	5	4	−3
	a_3	2	3	−4

  a. Use dominance to reduce the game to a 2 × 2 game. What strategies are dominated?
  b. Determine the optimal mixed strategy solution.
  c. What is the value of the game?

15. In a gambling game, Player A and Player B both have a $1 and a $5 bill. Each player selects one of the bills without the other player knowing the bill selected. Simultaneously they both reveal the bills selected. If the bills do not match, Player A wins Player B's bill. If the bills match, Player B wins Player A's bill.
  a. Develop the game theory table for this game. The values should be expressed as the gains (or losses) for Player A.
  b. Is there a pure strategy? Why or why not?
  c. Determine the optimal strategies and the value of this game. Does the game favor one player over the other?
  d. Suppose Player B decides to deviate from the optimal strategy and begins playing each bill 50% of the time. What should Player A do to improve Player A's winnings? Comment on why it is important to follow an optimal game theory strategy.

16. Two companies compete for a share of the soft drink market. Each worked with an advertising agency in order to develop alternative advertising strategies for the coming year. A variety of television advertisements, product promotions, in-store displays, and so on provides four different strategies for each company. The following table summarizes the projected change in market share for Company A once the two companies select their advertising strategy for the coming year. What is the optimal solution to this game for each of the players? What is the value of the game?

		Company B			
		b_1	b_2	b_3	b_4
Company A	a_1	3	0	2	4
	a_2	2	−2	1	0
	a_3	4	2	5	6
	a_4	−2	6	−1	0

Multicriteria Decisions

CONTENTS

In previous chapters we showed how a variety of quantitative methods can help managers make better decisions. Whenever we desired an optimal solution, we utilized a single criterion (e.g., maximize profit, minimize cost, minimize time). In this chapter we discuss techniques that are appropriate for situations in which the decision maker needs to consider multiple criteria in arriving at the overall best decision. For example, consider a company involved in selecting a location for a new manufacturing plant. The cost of land and construction may vary from location to location, so one criterion in selecting the best site could be the cost involved in building the plant; if cost were the sole criterion of interest, management would simply select the location that minimizes land cost plus construction cost. Before making any decision, however, management might also want to consider additional criteria such as the availability of transportation from the plant to the firm's distribution centers, the attractiveness of the proposed location in terms of hiring and retaining employees, energy costs at the proposed site, and state and local taxes. In such situations the complexity of the problem increases because one location may be more desirable in terms of one criterion and less desirable in terms of one or more of the other criteria.

To introduce the topic of multicriteria decision making, we consider a technique referred to as **goal programming.** This technique has been developed to handle multiple-criteria situations within the general framework of linear programming. We next consider a *scoring model* as a relatively easy way to identify the best decision alternative for a multicriteria problem. Finally, we introduce a method known as the *analytical hierarchy process (AHP),* which allows the user to make pairwise comparisons among the criteria and a series of pairwise comparisons among the decision alternatives in order to arrive at a prioritized ranking of the decision alternatives.

17.1 GOAL PROGRAMMING: FORMULATION AND GRAPHICAL SOLUTION

To illustrate the goal programming approach to multicriteria decision problems, let us consider a problem facing Nicolo Investment Advisors. A client has $80,000 to invest and, as an initial strategy, would like the investment portfolio restricted to two stocks:

Stock	Price/Share	Estimated Annual Return/Share	Risk Index/Share
U.S. Oil	$25	$3	0.50
Hub Properties	$50	$5	0.25

U.S. Oil, which has a return of $3 on a $25 share price, provides an annual rate of return of 12%, whereas Hub Properties provides an annual rate of return of 10%. The risk index per share, 0.50 for U.S. Oil and 0.25 for Hub Properties, is a rating Nicolo assigned to measure the relative risk of the two investments. Higher risk index values imply greater risk; hence, Nicolo judged U.S. Oil to be the riskier investment. By specifying a maximum portfolio risk index, Nicolo will avoid placing too much of the portfolio in high-risk investments.

To illustrate how to use the risk index per share to measure the total portfolio risk, suppose that Nicolo chooses a portfolio that invests all $80,000 in U.S. Oil, the higher risk, but higher return, investment. Nicolo could purchase $80,000/$25 = 3200 shares of U.S. Oil, and the portfolio would have a risk index of 3200(0.50) = 1600. Conversely, if Nicolo purchases no shares of either stock, the portfolio will have no risk, but also no return. Thus, the portfolio risk index will vary from 0 (least risk) to 1600 (most risk).

Nicolo's client would like to avoid a high-risk portfolio; thus, investing all funds in U.S. Oil would not be desirable. However, the client agreed that an acceptable level of risk would correspond to portfolios with a maximum total risk index of 700. Thus, considering only risk, one *goal* is to find a portfolio with a risk index of 700 or less.

Another goal of the client is to obtain an annual return of at least $9000. This goal can be achieved with a portfolio consisting of 2000 shares of U.S. Oil [at a cost of 2000($25) = $50,000] and 600 shares of Hub Properties [at a cost of 600($50) = $30,000]; the annual return in this case would be 2000($3) + 600($5) = $9000. Note, however, that the portfolio risk index for this investment strategy would be 2000(0.50) + 600(0.25) = 1150; thus, this portfolio achieves the annual return goal but does not satisfy the portfolio risk index goal.

Thus, the portfolio selection problem is a multicriteria decision problem involving two conflicting goals: one dealing with risk and one dealing with annual return. The goal programming approach was developed precisely for this kind of problem. Goal programming can be used to identify a portfolio that comes closest to achieving both goals. Before applying the methodology, the client must determine which, if either, goal is more important.

Suppose that the client's top-priority goal is to restrict the risk; that is, keeping the portfolio risk index at 700 or less is so important that the client is not willing to trade the achievement of this goal for any amount of an increase in annual return. As long as the portfolio risk index does not exceed 700, the client seeks the best possible return. Based on this statement of priorities, the goals for the problem are as follows:

Primary Goal (Priority Level 1)

Goal 1:   Find a portfolio that has a risk index of 700 or less.

Secondary Goal (Priority Level 2)

Goal 2:   Find a portfolio that will provide an annual return of at least $9000.

In goal programming with preemptive priorities, we never permit trade-offs between higher and lower level goals.

The primary goal is called a *priority level 1 goal,* and the secondary goal is called a *priority level 2 goal.* In goal programming terminology, these are called **preemptive priorities** because the decision maker is not willing to sacrifice any amount of achievement of the priority level 1 goal for the lower priority goal. The portfolio risk index of 700 is the **target value** for the priority level 1 (primary) goal, and the annual return of $9000 is the target value for the priority level 2 (secondary) goal. The difficulty in finding a solution that will achieve these goals is that only $80,000 is available for investment.

Developing the Constraints and the Goal Equations

We begin by defining the decision variables:

$$U = \text{number of shares of U.S. Oil purchased}$$
$$H = \text{number of shares of Hub Properties purchased}$$

Constraints for goal programming problems are handled in the same way as in an ordinary linear programming problem. In the Nicolo Investment Advisors problem, one constraint corresponds to the funds available. Because each share of U.S. Oil costs $25 and each share of Hub Properties costs $50, the constraint representing the funds available is

$$25U + 50H \leq 80,000$$

To complete the formulation of the model, we must develop a **goal equation** for each goal. Let us begin by writing the goal equation for the primary goal. Each share of U.S. Oil has a risk index of 0.50 and each share of Hub Properties has a risk index of 0.25; therefore, the portfolio risk index is $0.50U + 0.25H$. Depending on the values of U and H, the portfolio risk index may be less than, equal to, or greater than the target value of 700. To represent these possibilities mathematically, we create the goal equation

$$0.50U + 0.25H = 700 + d_1^+ - d_1^-$$

where

d_1^+ = the amount by which the portfolio risk index exceeds the target value of 700

d_1^- = the amount by which the portfolio risk index is less than the target value of 700

To achieve a goal exactly, the two deviation variables must both equal zero.

In goal programming, d_1^+ and d_1^- are called **deviation variables.** The purpose of deviation variables is to allow for the possibility of not meeting the target value exactly. Consider, for example, a portfolio that consists of $U = 2000$ shares of U.S. Oil and $H = 0$ shares of Hub Properties. The portfolio risk index is $0.50(2000) + 0.25(0) = 1000$. In this case, $d_1^+ = 300$ reflects the fact that the portfolio risk index exceeds the target value by 300 units; note also that since d_1^+ is greater than zero, the value of d_1^- must be zero. For a portfolio consisting of $U = 0$ shares of U.S. Oil and $H = 1000$ shares of Hub Properties, the portfolio risk index would be $0.50(0) + 0.25(1000) = 250$. In this case, $d_1^- = 450$ and $d_1^+ = 0$, indicating that the solution provides a portfolio risk index of 450 less than the target value of 700.

In general, the letter d is used for deviation variables in a goal programming model. A superscript of plus $(+)$ or minus $(-)$ is used to indicate whether the variable corresponds to a positive or negative deviation from the target value. If we bring the deviation variables to the left-hand side, we can rewrite the goal equation for the primary goal as

$$0.50U + 0.25H - d_1^+ + d_1^- = 700$$

Note that the value on the right-hand side of the goal equation is the target value for the goal. The left-hand side of the goal equation consists of two parts:

1. A function that defines the amount of goal achievement in terms of the decision variables (e.g., $0.50U + 0.25H$)
2. Deviation variables representing the difference between the target value for the goal and the level achieved

To develop a goal equation for the secondary goal, we begin by writing a function representing the annual return for the investment:

$$\text{Annual return} = 3U + 5H$$

Then we define two deviation variables that represent the amount of over- or underachievement of the goal. Doing so, we obtain

d_2^+ = the amount by which the annual return for the portfolio is greater than the target value of \$9000

d_2^- = the amount by which the annual return for the portfolio is less than the target value of \$9000

Using these two deviation variables, we write the goal equation for goal 2 as

$$3U + 5H = 9000 + d_2^+ - d_2^-$$

or

$$3U + 5H - d_2^+ + d_2^- = 9000$$

This step completes the development of the goal equations and the constraints for the Nicolo portfolio problem. We are now ready to develop an appropriate objective function for the problem.

Developing an Objective Function with Preemptive Priorities

The objective function in a goal programming model calls for minimizing a function of the deviation variables. In the portfolio selection problem, the most important goal, denoted P_1, is to find a portfolio with a risk index of 700 or less. This problem has only two goals, and the client is unwilling to accept a portfolio risk index greater than 700 to achieve the secondary annual return goal. Therefore, the secondary goal is denoted P_2. As we stated previously, these goal priorities are referred to as preemptive priorities because the satisfaction of a higher level goal cannot be traded for the satisfaction of a lower level goal.

Goal programming problems with preemptive priorities are solved by treating priority level 1 goals (P_1) first in an objective function. The idea is to start by finding a solution that comes closest to satisfying the priority level 1 goals. This solution is then modified by solving a problem with an objective function involving only priority level 2 goals (P_2); however, revisions in the solution are permitted only if they do not hinder achievement of the P_1 goals. In general, solving a goal programming problem with preemptive priorities involves solving a sequence of linear programs with different objective functions; P_1 goals are considered first, P_2 goals second, P_3 goals third, and so on. At each stage of the procedure, a revision in the solution is permitted only if it causes no reduction in the achievement of a higher priority goal.

We must solve one linear program for each priority level.

The number of linear programs that we must solve in sequence to develop the solution to a goal programming problem is determined by the number of priority levels. One linear program must be solved for each priority level. We will call the first linear program solved the priority level 1 problem, the second linear program solved the priority level 2 problem, and so on. Each linear program is obtained from the one at the next higher level by changing the objective function and adding a constraint.

We first formulate the objective function for the priority level 1 problem. The client stated that the portfolio risk index should not exceed 700. Is underachieving the target value of 700 a concern? Clearly, the answer is no because portfolio risk index values of less than 700 correspond to less risk. Is overachieving the target value of 700 a concern? The answer is yes because portfolios with a risk index greater than 700 correspond to unacceptable levels of risk. Thus, the objective function corresponding to the priority level 1 linear program should minimize the value of d_1^+.

The goal equations and the funds available constraint have already been developed. Thus, the priority level 1 linear program can now be stated.

P_1 Problem

$$\text{Min} \quad d_1^+$$
$$\text{s.t.}$$

$$
\begin{array}{rlll}
25U + 50H & & \leq 80{,}000 & \text{Funds available} \\
0.50U + 0.25H - d_1^+ + d_1^- & & = 700 & P_1 \text{ goal} \\
3U + 5H & - d_2^+ + d_2^- & = 9000 & P_2 \text{ goal} \\
U, H, d_1^+, d_1^-, d_2^+, d_2^- & \geq 0 &
\end{array}
$$

One approach that can often be used to solve a difficult problem is to break the problem into two or more smaller or easier problems. The linear programming procedure we use to solve the goal programming problem is based on this approach.

Graphical Solution Procedure

The graphical solution procedure for goal programming is similar to that for linear programming presented in Chapter 6. The only difference is that the procedure for goal programming involves a separate solution for each priority level. Recall that the linear programming graphical solution procedure uses a graph to display the values for the decision variables. Because the decision variables are nonnegative, we consider only that portion of the graph where $U \geq 0$ and $H \geq 0$. Recall also that every point on the graph is called a *solution point*.

We begin the graphical solution procedure for the Nicolo Investment problem by identifying all solution points that satisfy the available funds constraint:

$$25U + 50H \leq 80,000$$

The shaded region in Figure 17.1, feasible portfolios, consists of all points that satisfy this constraint—that is, values of U and H for which $25U + 50H \leq 80,000$.

The objective for the priority level 1 linear program is to minimize d_1^+, the amount by which the portfolio index exceeds the target value of 700. Recall that the P_1 goal equation is

$$0.50U + 0.25H - d_1^+ + d_1^- = 700$$

When the P_1 goal is met exactly, $d_1^+ = 0$ and $d_1^- = 0$; the goal equation then reduces to $0.50U + 0.25H = 700$. Figure 17.2 shows the graph of this equation; the shaded region identifies all solution points that satisfy the available funds constraint and also result in the value of $d_1^+ = 0$. Thus, the shaded region contains all the feasible solution points that achieve the priority level 1 goal.

At this point, we solved the priority level 1 problem. Note that alternative optimal solutions are possible; in fact, all solution points in the shaded region in Figure 17.2 maintain a portfolio risk index of 700 or less, and hence $d_1^+ = 0$.

The priority level 2 goal for the Nicolo Investment problem is to find a portfolio that will provide an annual return of at least $9000. Is overachieving the target value of $9000 a concern? Clearly, the answer is no because portfolios with an annual return of more than $9000 correspond to higher returns. Is underachieving the target value of $9000 a concern? The answer is yes because portfolios with an annual return of less than $9000 are not acceptable to the client. Thus, the objective function corresponding to the priority level 2 linear program should minimize the value of d_2^-. However, because goal 2 is a secondary goal, the solution to the priority level 2 linear program must not degrade the optimal solution to the priority level 1 problem. Thus, the priority level 2 linear program can now be stated.

FIGURE 17.1   PORTFOLIOS THAT SATISFY THE AVAILABLE FUNDS CONSTRAINT

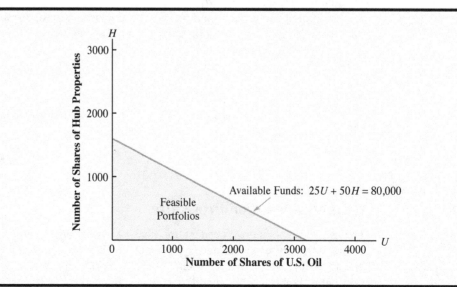

FIGURE 17.2   PORTFOLIOS THAT SATISFY THE P_1 GOAL

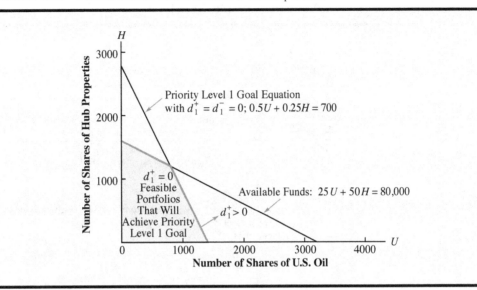

P_2 Problem

$$\text{Min} \qquad d_2^-$$

s.t.

$$
\begin{array}{rlcl}
25U + 50H & & \leq & 80{,}000 \quad \text{Funds available} \\
0.50U + 0.25H - d_1^+ + d_1^- & & = & 700 \quad P_1 \text{ goal} \\
3U + 5H & - d_2^+ + d_2^- & = & 9000 \quad P_2 \text{ goal} \\
d_1^+ & & = & 0 \quad \text{Maintain achievement} \\
& & & \qquad \text{of } P_1 \text{ goal}
\end{array}
$$

$$U, H, d_1^+, d_1^-, d_2^+, d_2^- \geq 0$$

Note that the priority level 2 linear program differs from the priority level 1 linear program in two ways. The objective function involves minimizing the amount by which the portfolio annual return underachieves the level 2 goal, and another constraint has been added to ensure that no amount of achievement of the priority level 1 goal is sacrificed.

Let us now continue the graphical solution procedure. The goal equation for the priority level 2 goal is

$$3U + 5H - d_2^+ + d_2^- = 9000$$

When both d_2^+ and d_2^- equal zero, this equation reduces to $3U + 5H = 9000$; we show the graph with this equation in Figure 17.3.

At this stage, we cannot consider any solution point that will degrade the achievement of the priority level 1 goal. Figure 17.3 shows that no solution points will achieve the priority level 2 goal and maintain the values we were able to achieve for the priority level 1 goal. In fact, the best solution that can be obtained when considering the priority level 2 goal is given by the point ($U = 800, H = 1200$); in other words, this point comes the closest to satisfying the priority level 2 goal from among those solutions satisfying the priority level 1 goal. Because the annual return corresponding to this solution point is $3(800) + $5(1200) = 8400, identifying a portfolio that will satisfy both the priority level 1 and the

FIGURE 17.3   BEST SOLUTION WITH RESPECT TO BOTH GOALS
(SOLUTION TO P_2 PROBLEM)

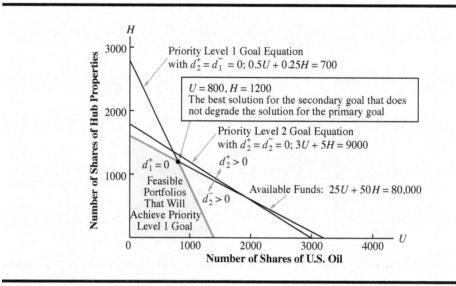

priority level 2 goals is impossible. In fact, the best solution underachieves goal 2 by $d_2^- = $9000 - $8400 = 600.

Thus, the goal programming solution for the Nicolo Investment problem recommends that the $80,000 available for investment be used to purchase 800 shares of U.S. Oil and 1200 shares of Hub Properties. Note that the priority level 1 goal of a portfolio risk index of 700 or less has been achieved. However, the priority level 2 goal of at least a $9000 annual return is not achievable. The annual return for the recommended portfolio is $8400.

In summary, the graphical solution procedure for goal programming involves the following steps.

Step 1.   Identify the feasible solution points that satisfy the problem constraints.
Step 2.   Identify all feasible solutions that achieve the highest-priority goal; if no feasible solutions will achieve the highest-priority goal, identify the solution(s) that comes closest to achieving it.
Step 3.   Move down one priority level, and determine the "best" solution possible without sacrificing any achievement of higher priority goals.
Step 4.   Repeat step 3 until all priority levels have been considered.

Problem 2 will test your ability to formulate a goal programming model and use the graphical solution procedure to obtain a solution.

Although the graphical solution procedure is a convenient method for solving goal programming problems involving two decision variables, the solution of larger problems requires a computer-aided approach. In Section 17.2 we illustrate how to use a computer software package to solve more complex goal programming problems.

Goal Programming Model

As we stated, preemptive goal programming problems are solved as a sequence of linear programs: one linear program for each priority level. However, notation that permits writing a goal programming problem in one concise statement is helpful.

In writing the overall objective for the portfolio selection problem, we must write the objective function in a way that reminds us of the preemptive priorities. We can do so by writing the objective function as

$$\text{Min}\quad P_1(d_1^+) + P_2(d_2^-)$$

The priority levels P_1 and P_2 are not numerical weights on the deviation variables, but simply labels that remind us of the priority levels for the goals.

We now write the complete goal programming model as

$$\text{Min}\quad P_1(d_1^+) + P_2(d_2^-)$$
s.t.

$25U +$	$50H$		$\leq 80{,}000$	Funds available
$0.50U + 0.25H - d_1^+ + d_1^-$			$= 700$	P_1 goal
$3U +$	$5H$	$- d_2^+ + d_2^-$	$= 9000$	P_2 goal

$$U, H, d_1^+, d_1^-, d_2^+, d_2^- \geq 0$$

With the exception of the P_1 and P_2 priority levels in the objective function, this model is a linear programming model. The solution of this linear program involves solving a sequence of linear programs involving goals at decreasing priority levels.

We now summarize the procedure used to develop a goal programming model.

Step 1. Identify the goals and any constraints that reflect resource capacities or other restrictions that may prevent achievement of the goals.
Step 2. Determine the priority level of each goal; goals with priority level P_1 are most important, those with priority level P_2 are next most important, and so on.
Step 3. Define the decision variables.
Step 4. Formulate the constraints in the usual linear programming fashion.
Step 5. For each goal, develop a goal equation, with the right-hand side specifying the target value for the goal. Deviation variables d_i^+ and d_i^- are included in each goal equation to reflect the possible deviations above or below the target value.
Step 6. Write the objective function in terms of minimizing a prioritized function of the deviation variables.

NOTES AND COMMENTS

1. The constraints in the general goal programming model are of two types: goal equations and ordinary linear programming constraints. Some analysts call the goal equations *goal constraints* and the ordinary linear programming constraints *system constraints.*
2. You might think of the general goal programming model as having "hard" and "soft" constraints. The hard constraints are the ordinary linear programming constraints that cannot be violated. The soft constraints are the ones resulting from the goal equations. Soft constraints can be vio-

lated but with a penalty for doing so. The penalty is reflected by the coefficient of the deviation variable in the objective function. In Section 17.2 we illustrate this point with a problem that has a coefficient of 2 for one of the deviation variables.
3. Note that the constraint added in moving from the linear programming problem at one priority level to the linear programming problem at the next lower priority level becomes a hard constraint. No amount of achievement of a higher priority goal may be sacrificed to achieve a lower priority goal.

17.2 GOAL PROGRAMMING: SOLVING MORE COMPLEX PROBLEMS

In Section 17.1 we formulated and solved a goal programming model that involved one priority level 1 goal and one priority level 2 goal. In this section we show how to formulate and solve goal programming models that involve multiple goals within the same priority level. Although specially developed computer programs can solve goal programming models, these programs are not as readily available as general purpose linear programming software packages. Thus, the computer solution procedure outlined in this section develops a solution to a goal programming model by solving a sequence of linear programming models with a general purpose linear programming software package.

Suncoast Office Supplies Problem

The management of Suncoast Office Supplies establishes monthly goals, or quotas, for the types of customers contacted. For the next four weeks, Suncoast's customer contact strategy calls for the salesforce, which consists of four salespeople, to make 200 contacts with established customers who have previously purchased supplies from the firm. In addition, the strategy calls for 120 contacts of new customers. The purpose of this latter goal is to ensure that the salesforce is continuing to investigate new sources of sales.

After making allowances for travel and waiting time, as well as for demonstration and direct sales time, Suncoast allocated two hours of salesforce effort to each contact of an established customer. New customer contacts tend to take longer and require three hours per contact. Normally, each salesperson works 40 hours per week, or 160 hours over the four-week planning horizon; under a normal work schedule, the four salespeople will have $4(160) = 640$ hours of salesforce time available for customer contacts.

Management is willing to use some overtime, if needed, but is also willing to accept a solution that uses less than the scheduled 640 hours available. However, management wants both overtime and underutilization of the workforce limited to no more than 40 hours over the four-week period. Thus, in terms of overtime, management's goal is to use no more than $640 + 40 = 680$ hours of salesforce time; and in terms of labor utilization, management's goal is to use at least $640 - 40 = 600$ hours of salesforce time.

In addition to the customer contact goals, Suncoast established a goal regarding sales volume. Based on its experience, Suncoast estimates that each established customer contacted will generate $250 of sales and that each new customer contacted will generate $125 of sales. Management wants to generate sales revenue of at least $70,000 for the next month.

Given Suncoast's small salesforce and the short time frame involved, management decided that the overtime goal and the labor utilization goal are both priority level 1 goals. Management also concluded that the $70,000 sales revenue goal should be a priority level 2 goal and that the two customer contact goals should be priority level 3 goals. Based on these priorities, we can now summarize the goals.

Priority Level 1 Goals

Goal 1: Do not use any more than 680 hours of salesforce time.

Goal 2: Do not use any less than 600 hours of salesforce time.

Priority Level 2 Goal

Goal 3: Generate sales revenue of at least $70,000.

Priority Level 3 Goals

Goal 4: Call on at least 200 established customers.

Goal 5: Call on at least 120 new customers.

Formulating the Goal Equations

Next, we must define the decision variables whose values will be used to determine whether we are able to achieve the goals. Let

$$E = \text{the number of established customers contacted}$$
$$N = \text{the number of new customers contacted}$$

Using these decision variables and appropriate deviation variables, we can develop a goal equation for each goal. The procedure used parallels the approach introduced in the preceding section. A summary of the results obtained is shown for each goal.

Goal 1

$$2E + 3N - d_1^+ + d_1^- = 680$$

where

$d_1^+ = $ the amount by which the number of hours used by the salesforce is greater than the target value of 680 hours

$d_1^- = $ the amount by which the number of hours used by the salesforce is less than the target value of 680 hours

Goal 2

$$2E + 3N - d_2^+ + d_2^- = 600$$

where

$d_2^+ = $ the amount by which the number of hours used by the salesforce is greater than the target value of 600 hours

$d_2^- = $ the amount by which the number of hours used by the salesforce is less than the target value of 600 hours

Goal 3

$$250E + 125N - d_3^+ + d_3^- = 70{,}000$$

where

$d_3^+ = $ the amount by which the sales revenue is greater than the target value of \$70,000

$d_3^- = $ the amount by which the sales revenue is less than the target value of \$70,000

Goal 4

$$E - d_4^+ + d_4^- = 200$$

where

$d_4^+ = $ the amount by which the number of established customer contacts is greater than the target value of 200 established customer contacts

$d_4^- = $ the amount by which the number of established customer contacts is less than the target value of 200 established customer contacts

Goal 5

$$N - d_5^+ + d_5^- = 120$$

where

d_5^+ = the amount by which the number of new customer contacts is greater than the target value of 120 new customer contacts

d_5^- = the amount by which the number of new customer contacts is less than the target value of 120 new customer contacts

Formulating the Objective Function

To develop the objective function for the Suncoast Office Supplies problem, we begin by considering the priority level 1 goals. When considering goal 1, if $d_1^+ = 0$, we will have found a solution that uses no more than 680 hours of salesforce time. Because solutions for which d_1^+ is greater than zero represent overtime beyond the desired level, the objective function should minimize the value of d_1^+. When considering goal 2, if $d_2^- = 0$, we will have found a solution that uses *at least* 600 hours of salesforce time. If d_2^- is greater than zero, however, labor utilization will not have reached the acceptable level. Thus, the objective function for the priority level 1 goals should minimize the value of d_2^-. Because both priority level 1 goals are equally important, the objective function for the priority level 1 problem is

$$\text{Min} \quad d_1^+ + d_2^-$$

In considering the priority level 2 goal, we note that management wants to achieve sales revenues of at least $70,000. If $d_3^- = 0$, Suncoast will achieve revenues of *at least* $70,000, and if $d_3^- > 0$, revenues of less than $70,000 will be obtained. Thus, the objective function for the priority level 2 problem is

$$\text{Min} \quad d_3^-$$

Next, we consider what the objective function must be for the priority level 3 problem. When considering goal 4, if $d_4^- = 0$, we will have found a solution with *at least* 200 established customer contacts; however, if $d_4^- > 0$, we will have underachieved the goal of contacting at least 200 established customers. Thus, for goal 4 the objective is to minimize d_4^-. When considering goal 5, if $d_5^- = 0$, we will have found a solution with *at least* 120 new customer contacts; however, if $d_5^- > 0$, we will have underachieved the goal of contacting at least 120 new customers. Thus, for goal 5 the objective is to minimize d_5^-. If both goals 4 and 5 are equal in importance, the objective function for the priority level 3 problem would be

$$\text{Min} \quad d_4^- + d_5^-$$

However, suppose that management believes that generating new customers is vital to the long-run success of the firm and that goal 5 should be weighted more than goal 4. If management believes that goal 5 is twice as important as goal 4, the objective function for the priority level 3 problem would be

$$\text{Min} \quad d_4^- + 2d_5^-$$

Combining the objective functions for all three priority levels, we obtain the overall objective function for the Suncoast Office Supplies problem:

$$\text{Min} \quad P_1(d_1^+) + P_1(d_2^-) + P_2(d_3^-) + P_3(d_4^-) + P_3(2d_5^-)$$

As we indicated previously, P_1, P_2, and P_3 are simply labels that remind us that goals 1 and 2 are the priority level 1 goals, goal 3 is the priority level 2 goal, and goals 4 and 5 are the priority level 3 goals. We can now write the complete goal programming model for the Suncoast Office Supplies problem as follows:

$$\text{Min} \quad P_1(d_1^+) + P_1(d_2^-) + P_2(d_3^-) + P_3(d_4^-) + P_3(2d_5^-)$$

s.t.

$2E +$	$3N$	$- d_1^+ + d_1^-$				$= 680$	Goal 1
$2E +$	$3N$	$- d_2^+ + d_2^-$				$= 600$	Goal 2
$250E + 125N$		$- d_3^+ + d_3^-$				$= 70{,}000$	Goal 3
E		$- d_4^+ + d_4^-$				$= 200$	Goal 4
	N	$- d_5^+ + d_5^- =$				120	Goal 5

$$E, N, d_1^+, d_1^-, d_2^+, d_2^-, d_3^+, d_3^-, d_4^+, d_4^-, d_5^+, d_5^- \geq 0$$

Computer Solution

The following computer procedure develops a solution to a goal programming model by solving a sequence of linear programming problems. The first problem comprises all the constraints and all the goal equations for the complete goal programming model; however, the objective function for this problem involves only the P_1 priority level goals. Again, we refer to this problem as the P_1 problem.

Whatever the solution to the P_1 problem, a P_2 problem is formed by adding a constraint to the P_1 model that ensures that subsequent problems will not degrade the solution obtained for the P_1 problem. The objective function for the priority level 2 problem takes into consideration only the P_2 goals. We continue the process until we have considered all priority levels. We illustrate the procedure for the Suncoast Office Supplies problem using the linear programming module of The Management Scientist software package.

To solve the Suncoast Office Supplies problem, we begin by solving the P_1 problem:

$$\text{Min} \quad d_1^+ + d_2^-$$

s.t.

$2E +$	$3N - d_1^+ + d_1^-$			$= 680$	Goal 1
$2E +$	$3N$	$- d_2^+ + d_2^-$		$= 600$	Goal 2
$250E + 125N$		$- d_3^+ + d_3^-$		$= 70{,}000$	Goal 3
E		$- d_4^+ + d_4^-$		$= 200$	Goal 4
	N	$- d_5^+ + d_5^- =$		120	Goal 5

$$E, N, d_1^+, d_1^-, d_2^+, d_2^-, d_3^+, d_3^-, d_4^+, d_4^-, d_5^+, d_5^- \geq 0$$

In Figure 17.4 we show The Management Scientist solution for this linear program. Note that D1PLUS refers to d_1^+, D2MINUS refers to d_2^-, D1MINUS refers to d_1^-, and so on. The solution shows $E = 250$ established customer contacts and $N = 60$ new customer contacts. Because D1PLUS = 0 and D2MINUS = 0, we see that the solution achieves both goals 1 and 2. Alternatively, the value of the objective function is 0, confirming that both priority level 1 goals have been achieved. Next, we consider goal 3, the priority level 2 goal, which is to minimize D3MINUS. The solution in Figure 17.4 shows that

FIGURE 17.4   THE MANAGEMENT SCIENTIST SOLUTION OF THE P_1 PROBLEM

```
Objective Function Value = 0.000

        Variable              Value              Reduced Costs
     --------------      ----------------     ------------------
        D1PLUS                0.000                  1.000
        D2MINUS               0.000                  1.000
        E                   250.000                  0.000
        N                    60.000                  0.000
        D1MINUS               0.000                  0.000
        D2PLUS               80.000                  0.000
        D3PLUS                0.000                  0.000
        D3MINUS               0.000                  0.000
        D4PLUS               50.000                  0.000
        D4MINUS               0.000                  0.000
        D5PLUS                0.000                  0.000
        D5MINUS              60.000                  0.000
```

D3MINUS = 0. Thus, the solution of $E = 250$ established customer contacts and $N = 60$ new customer contacts also achieves goal 3, the priority level 2 goal, which is to generate a sales revenue of at least $70,000. The fact that D3PLUS = 0 indicates that the current solution satisfies goal 3 exactly at $70,000. Finally, the solution in Figure 17.4 shows D4PLUS = 50 and D5MINUS = 60. These values tell us that goal 4 of the priority level 3 goals is overachieved by 50 established customers, but that goal 5 is underachieved by 60 new customers. As this point, both the priority level 1 and 2 goals have been achieved, but we need to solve another linear program to determine whether a solution can be identified that will satisfy both of the priority level 3 goals. Therefore, we go directly to the P_3 problem.

The linear programming model for the P_3 problem is a modification of the linear programming model for the P_1 problem. Specifically, the objective function for the P_3 problem is expressed in terms of the priority level 3 goals. Thus, the P_3 problem objective function becomes minimize D4MINUS + 2D5MINUS. The original five constraints of the P_1 problem appear in the P_3 problem. However, two additional constraints must be added to ensure that the solution to the P_3 problem continues to satisfy the priority level 1 and priority level 2 goals. Thus, we add the priority level 1 constraint D1PLUS + D2MINUS = 0 and the priority level 2 constraint D3MINUS = 0. Making these modifications to the P_1 problem, we obtain the solution to the P_3 problem shown in Figure 17.5.

Referring to Figure 17.5, we see the objective function value of 120 indicates that the priority level 3 goals cannot be achieved. Since D5MINUS = 60, the optimal solution of $E = 250$ and $N = 60$ results in 60 fewer new customer contacts than desired. However, the fact that we solved the P_3 problem tells us the goal programming solution comes as close as possible to satisfying priority level 3 goals given the achievement of both the priority level 1 and 2 goals. Because all priority levels have been considered, the solution procedure is finished. The optimal solution for Suncoast is to contact 250 established customers and 60 new customers. Although this solution will not achieve management's goal of contacting at least 120 new customers, it does achieve each of the other goals specified. If management isn't happy with this solution, a different set of priorities could be considered. Management must keep in mind, however, that in any situation involving multiple goals at different priority levels, rarely will all the goals be achieved with existing resources.

FIGURE 17.5   THE MANAGEMENT SCIENTIST SOLUTION OF THE P_3 PROBLEM

```
Objective Function Value = 120.000

        Variable              Value              Reduced Costs
        --------------    ---------------       -----------------
        D1PLUS                 0.000                 0.000
        D2MINUS                0.000                 1.000
        E                    250.000                 0.000
        N                     60.000                 0.000
        D1MINUS                0.000                 1.000
        D2PLUS                80.000                 0.000
        D3PLUS                 0.000                 0.008
        D3MINUS                0.000                 0.000
        D4PLUS                50.000                 0.000
        D4MINUS                0.000                 1.000
        D5PLUS                 0.000                 2.000
        D5MINUS               60.000                 0.000
```

NOTES AND COMMENTS

1. Not all goal programming problems involve multiple priority levels. For problems with one priority level, only one linear program needs to be solved to obtain the goal programming solution. The analyst simply minimizes the weighted deviations from the goals. Trade-offs are permitted among the goals because they are all at the same priority level.

2. The goal programming approach can be used when the analyst is confronted with an infeasible solution to an ordinary linear program. Reformulating some constraints as goal equations with deviation variables allows a solution that minimizes the weighted sum of the deviation variables. Often, this approach will suggest a reasonable solution.

3. The approach that we used to solve goal programming problems with multiple priority levels is to solve a sequence of linear programs. These linear programs are closely related so that complete reformulation and solution are not necessary. By changing the objective function and adding a constraint, we can go from one linear program to the next.

17.3   SCORING MODELS

A scoring model is a relatively quick and easy way to identify the best decision alternative for a multicriteria decision problem. We will demonstrate the use of a scoring model for a job selection application.

Assume that a graduating college student with a double major in finance and accounting received job offers for the following three positions:

- A financial analyst for an investment firm located in Chicago
- An accountant for a manufacturing firm located in Denver
- An auditor for a CPA firm located in Houston

When asked about which job is preferred, the student made the following comments: "The financial analyst position in Chicago provides the best opportunity for my long-run career advancement. However, I would prefer living in Denver rather than in Chicago or Houston. On the other hand, I liked the management style and philosophy at the Houston

CPA firm the best." The student's statement points out that this example is clearly a multi-criteria decision problem. Considering only the *long-run career advancement* criterion, the financial analyst position in Chicago is the preferred decision alternative. Considering only the *location* criterion, the best decision alternative is the accountant position in Denver. Finally, considering only the *management style* criterion, the best alternative is the auditor position with the CPA firm in Houston. For most individuals, a multicriteria decision problem that requires a trade-off among the several criteria is difficult to solve. In this section, we describe how a **scoring model** can assist in analyzing a multicriteria decision problem and help identify the preferred decision alternative.

The steps required to develop a scoring model are as follows:

Step 1. Develop a list of the criteria to be considered. The criteria are the factors that the decision maker considers relevant for evaluating each decision alternative.

A scoring model enables a decision maker to identify the criteria and indicate the weight or importance of each criterion.

Step 2. Assign a weight to each criterion that describes the criterion's relative importance. Let

$$w_i = \text{the weight for criterion } i$$

Step 3. Assign a rating for each criterion that shows how well each decision alternative satisfies the criterion. Let

$$r_{ij} = \text{the rating for criterion } i \text{ and decision alternative } j$$

Step 4. Compute the score for each decision alternative. Let

$$S_j = \text{score for decision alternative } j$$

The equation used to compute S_j is as follows:

$$S_j = \sum_i w_i r_{ij} \tag{17.1}$$

Step 5. Order the decision alternatives from the highest score to the lowest score to provide the scoring model's ranking of the decision alternatives. The decision alternative with the highest score is the recommended decision alternative.

Let us return to the multicriteria job selection problem the graduating student was facing and illustrate the use of a scoring model to assist in the decision-making process. In carrying out step 1 of the scoring model procedure, the student listed seven criteria as important factors in the decision-making process. These criteria are as follows:

- Career advancement
- Location
- Management style
- Salary
- Prestige
- Job security
- Enjoyment of the work

In step **2**, a weight is assigned to each criterion to indicate the criterion's relative importance in the decision-making process. For example, using a five-point scale, the question used to assign a weight to the career advancement criterion would be as follows:

Relative to the other criteria you are considering, how important is career advancement?

Importance	Weight
Very important	5
Somewhat important	4
Average importance	3
Somewhat unimportant	2
Very unimportant	1

By repeating this question for each of the seven criteria, the student provided the criterion weights shown in Table 17.1. Using this table, we see that career advancement and enjoyment of the work are the two most important criteria, each receiving a weight of 5. The management style and job security criteria are both considered somewhat important, and thus each received a weight of 4. Location and salary are considered average in importance, each receiving a weight of 3. Finally, because prestige is considered to be somewhat unimportant, it received a weight of 2.

The weights shown in Table 17.1 are subjective values provided by the student. A different student would most likely choose to weight the criteria differently. One of the key advantages of a scoring model is that it uses the subjective weights that most closely reflect the preferences of the individual decision maker.

In step 3, each decision alternative is rated in terms of how well it satisfies each criterion. For example, using a nine-point scale, the question used to assign a rating for the "financial analyst in Chicago" alternative and the career advancement criterion would be as follows:

To what extent does the financial analyst position in Chicago satisfy your career advancement criterion?

Level of Satisfaction	Rating
Extremely high	9
Very high	8
High	7
Slightly high	6
Average	5
Slightly low	4
Low	3
Very low	2
Extremely low	1

TABLE 17.1 WEIGHTS FOR THE SEVEN JOB SELECTION CRITERIA

Criterion	Importance	Weight (w_i)
Career advancement	Very important	5
Location	Average importance	3
Management style	Somewhat important	4
Salary	Average importance	3
Prestige	Somewhat unimportant	2
Job security	Somewhat important	4
Enjoyment of the work	Very important	5

A score of 8 on this question would indicate that the student believes the financial analyst position would be rated "very high" in terms of satisfying the career advancement criterion.

This scoring process must be completed for each combination of decision alternative and decision criterion. Because seven decision criteria and three decision alternatives need to be considered, $7 \times 3 = 21$ ratings must be provided. Table 17.2 summarizes the student's responses. Scanning this table provides some insights about how the student rates each decision criterion and decision alternative combination. For example, a rating of 9, corresponding to an extremely high level of satisfaction, only appears for the management style criterion and the auditor position in Houston. Thus, considering all combinations, the student rates the auditor position in Houston as the very best in terms of satisfying the management criterion. The lowest rating in the table is a 3 that appears for the location criterion of the financial analyst position in Chicago. This rating indicates that Chicago is rated "low" in terms of satisfying the student's location criterion. Other insights and interpretations are possible, but the question at this point is how a scoring model uses the data in Tables 17.1 and 17.2 to identify the best overall decision alternative.

Step 4 of the procedure shows that equation (17.1) is used to compute the score for each decision alternative. The data in Table 17.1 provide the weight for each criterion (w_i) and the data in Table 17.2 provide the ratings of each decision alternative for each criterion (r_{ij}). Thus, for decision alternative 1, the score for the financial analyst position in Chicago is

By comparing the scores for each criterion, a decision maker can learn why a particular decision alternative has the highest score.

$$S_1 = \sum_i w_i r_{i1} = 5(8) + 3(3) + 4(5) + 3(6) + 2(7) + 4(4) + 5(8) = 157$$

The scores for the other decision alternatives are computed in the same manner. The computations are summarized in Table 17.3.

Problem 9 provides more practice with this scoring model.

From Table 17.3, we see that the highest score of 167 corresponds to the accountant position in Denver. Thus, the accountant position in Denver is the recommended decision alternative. The financial analyst position in Chicago, with a score of 157, is ranked second, and the auditor position in Houston, with a score of 149, is ranked third.

The job selection example that illustrates the use of a scoring model involved seven criteria, each of which was assigned a weight from 1 to 5. In other applications the weights assigned to the criteria may be percentages that reflect the importance of each of the criteria. In addition, multicriteria problems often involve additional subcriteria that enable the decision maker to incorporate additional detail into the decision process. For instance, con-

TABLE 17.2 RATINGS FOR EACH DECISION CRITERION AND EACH DECISION ALTERNATIVE COMBINATION

	Decision Alternative		
Criterion	Financial Analyst Chicago	Accountant Denver	Auditor Houston
Career advancement	8	6	4
Location	3	8	7
Management style	5	6	9
Salary	6	7	5
Prestige	7	5	4
Job security	4	7	6
Enjoyment of the work	8	6	5

TABLE 17.3 COMPUTATION OF SCORES FOR THE THREE DECISION ALTERNATIVES

| | | Decision Alternative | | | | | |
| | | Financial Analyst Chicago | | Accountant Denver | | Auditor Houston | |
Criterion	Weight w_i	Rating r_{i1}	Score $w_i r_{i1}$	Rating r_{i2}	Score $w_i r_{i2}$	Rating r_{i3}	Score $w_i r_{i3}$
Career advancement	5	8	40	6	30	4	20
Location	3	3	9	8	24	7	21
Management style	4	5	20	6	24	9	36
Salary	3	6	18	7	21	5	15
Prestige	2	7	14	5	10	4	8
Job security	4	4	16	7	28	6	24
Enjoyment of the work	5	8	40	6	30	5	25
Score			157		167		149

sider the location criterion in the job selection example. This criterion might be further subdivided into the following three subcriteria:

- Affordability of housing
- Recreational opportunities
- Climate

In this case, the three subcriteria would have to be assigned weights, and a score for each decision alternative would have to be computed for each subcriterion. Q.M. in Action, Scoring Model at Ford Motor Company, illustrates how scoring models can be applied for a problem involving four criteria, each of which has several subcriteria. This example also demonstrates the use of percentage weights for the criteria and the wide applicability of scoring models in more complex problem situations.

Q.M. IN ACTION

SCORING MODEL AT FORD MOTOR COMPANY*

Ford Motor Company needed benchmark data in order to set performance targets for future and current model automobiles. A detailed proposal was developed and sent to five suppliers. Three suppliers were considered acceptable for the project.

Because the three suppliers had different capabilities in terms of teardown analysis and testing, Ford developed three project alternatives:

Alternative 1: Supplier C does the entire project alone.

Alternative 2: Supplier A does the testing portion of the project and works with Supplier B to complete the remaining parts of the project.

Alternative 3: Supplier A does the testing portion of the project and works with Supplier C to complete the remaining parts of the project.

For routine projects, selecting the lowest cost alternative might be appropriate. However, because this project involved many nonroutine tasks, Ford incorporated four criteria into the decision process.

The four criteria selected by Ford are as follows:

1. Skill level (effective project leader and a skilled team)
2. Cost containment (ability to stay within approved budget)
3. Timing containment (ability to meet program timing requirements)
4. Hardware display (location and functionality of teardown center and user friendliness)

(continued)

Using team consensus, a weight of 25% was assigned to each of these criteria; note that these weights indicate that members of the Ford project team considered each criterion to be equally important in the decision process.

Each of the four criteria was further subdivided into subcriteria. For example, the skill-level criterion had four subcriteria: project manager leadership; team structure organization; team players' communication; and past Ford experience. In total, 17 subcriteria were considered. A team-consensus weighting process was used to develop percentage weights for the subcriteria. The weights assigned to the skill-level subcriteria were 40% for project manager leadership; 20% for team structure organization; 20% for team players' communication; and 20% for past Ford experience.

Team members visited all the suppliers and individually rated them for each subcriterion using a 1–10 scale (1-worst, 10-best). Then, in a team meeting, consensus ratings were developed. For Alternative 1, the consensus ratings developed for the skill-level subcriteria were 8 for project manager leadership; 8 for team structure organization; 7 for team players' communication; and 8 for past Ford

experience. Because the weights assigned to the skill-level subcriteria are 40%, 20%, 20%, and 20%, the rating for Alternative 1 corresponding to the skill-level criterion is

$$\text{Rating} = .4(8) + .2(8) + .2(7) + .2(8) = 7.8$$

In a similar fashion, ratings for Alternative 1 corresponding to each of the other criteria were developed. The results obtained were a rating of 6.8 for cost containment, 6.65 for timing containment, and 8 for hardware display. Using the initial weights of 25% assigned to each criterion, the final rating for Alternative $1 = .25(7.8) + .25(6.8) + .25(6.65) + .25(8) = 7.3$. In a similar fashion, a final rating of 7.4 was developed for Alternative 2, and a final rating of 7.5 was developed for Alternative 3. Thus, Alternative 3 was the recommended decision. Subsequent sensitivity analysis on the weights assigned to the criteria showed that Alternative 3 still received equal or higher ratings than Alternative 1 or Alternative 2. These results increased the team's confidence that Alternative 3 was the best choice.

*Based on Senthil A. Gurusami, "Ford's Wrenching Decision," *OR/MS Today* (December 1998): 36–39.

17.4 ANALYTIC HIERARCHY PROCESS

The **analytic hierarchy process (AHP),** developed by Thomas L. Saaty,[1] is designed to solve complex multicriteria decision problems. AHP requires the decision maker to provide judgments about the relative importance of each criterion and then specify a preference for each decision alternative using each criterion. The output of AHP is a prioritized ranking of the decision alternatives based on the overall preferences expressed by the decision maker.

To introduce AHP, we consider a car purchasing decision problem faced by Diane Payne. After a preliminary analysis of the makes and models of several used cars, Diane narrowed her list of decision alternatives to three cars: a Honda Accord, a Saturn, and a Chevrolet Cavalier. Table 17.4 summarizes the information Diane collected about these cars.

Diane decided that the following criteria were relevant for her car selection decision process:

- Price
- Miles per gallon (MPG)
- Comfort
- Style

Data regarding the Price and MPG are provided in Table 17.4. However, measures of the Comfort and Style cannot be specified so directly. Diane will need to consider factors such as the car's interior, type of audio system, ease of entry, seat adjustments, and driver visibility in order to determine the comfort level of each car. The style criterion will have to be based on Diane's subjective evaluation of the color and the general appearance of each car.

---

[1]T. Saaty, *Decision Making for Leaders: The Analytic Hierarchy Process for Decisions in a Complex World,* 3d. ed., RWS, 1999.

TABLE 17.4   INFORMATION FOR THE CAR SELECTION PROBLEM

| | Decision Alternative | | |
Characteristics	Accord	Saturn	Cavalier
Price	$13,100	$11,200	$9500
Color	Black	Red	Blue
Miles per gallon	19	23	28
Interior	Deluxe	Above Average	Standard
Body type	4-door midsize	2-door sport	2-door compact
Sound system	AM/FM, tape, CD	AM/FM	AM/FM

AHP allows a decision maker to express personal preferences and subjective judgments about the various aspects of a multicriteria problem.

Even when a criterion such as price can be easily measured, subjectivity becomes an issue whenever a decision maker indicates his or her personal preference for the decision alternatives based on price. For instance, the price of the Accord ($13,100) is $3600 more than the price of the Cavalier ($9500). The $3600 difference might represent a great deal of money to one person, but not much of a difference to another person. Thus, whether the Accord is considered "extremely more expensive" than the Cavalier or perhaps only "moderately more expensive" than the Cavalier depends upon the financial status and the subjective opinion of the person making the comparison. An advantage of AHP is that it can handle situations in which the unique subjective judgments of the individual decision maker constitute an important part of the decision-making process.

Developing the Hierarchy

The first step in AHP is to develop a graphical representation of the problem in terms of the overall goal, the criteria to be used, and the decision alternatives. Such a graph depicts the **hierarchy** for the problem. Figure 17.6 shows the hierarchy for the car selection problem. Note that the first level of the hierarchy shows that the overall goal is to select the best car. At the second level, the four criteria (Price, MPG, Comfort, and Style) each contribute to the achievement of the overall goal. Finally, at the third level, each decision alternative—Accord, Saturn, and Cavalier—contributes to each criterion in a unique way.

Using AHP, the decision maker specifies judgments about the relative importance of each of the four criteria in terms of its contribution to the achievement of the overall goal.

FIGURE 17.6   HIERARCHY FOR THE CAR SELECTION PROBLEM

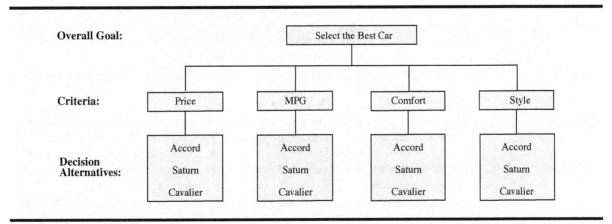

At the next level, the decision maker indicates a preference for each decision alternative based on each criterion. A mathematical process is used to synthesize the information on the relative importance of the criteria and the preferences for the decision alternatives to provide an overall priority ranking of the decision alternatives. In the car selection problem, AHP will use Diane's personal preferences to provide a priority ranking of the three cars in terms of how well each car meets the overall goal of being the *best* car.

17.5   ESTABLISHING PRIORITIES USING AHP

In this section we show how AHP uses pairwise comparisons expressed by the decision maker to establish priorities for the criteria and priorities for the decision alternatives based on each criterion. Using the car selection example, we show how AHP determines priorities for each of the following:

1. How the four criteria contribute to the overall goal of selecting the best car
2. How the three cars compare using the Price criterion
3. How the three cars compare using the MPG criterion
4. How the three cars compare using the Comfort criterion
5. How the three cars compare using the Style criterion

In the following discussion, we demonstrate how to establish priorities for the four criteria in terms of how each contributes to the overall goal of selecting the best car. The priorities of the three cars using each criterion can be determined similarly.

Pairwise Comparisons

Pairwise comparisons form the fundamental building blocks of AHP. In establishing the priorities for the four criteria, AHP will require Diane to state how important each criterion is relative to each other criterion when the criteria are compared two at a time (pairwise). That is, with the four criteria (Price, MPG, Comfort, and Style) Diane must make the following pairwise comparisons:

> Price compared to MPG
>
> Price compared to Comfort
>
> Price compared to Style
>
> MPG compared to Comfort
>
> MPG compared to Style
>
> Comfort compared to Style

In each comparison, Diane must select the more important criterion and then express a judgment of how much more important the selected criterion is.

For example, in the Price-MPG pairwise comparison, assume that Diane indicates that Price is more important than MPG. To measure how much more important Price is compared to MPG, AHP uses a scale with values from 1 to 9. Table 17.5 shows how the decision maker's verbal description of the relative importance between the two criteria are converted into a numerical rating. In the car selection example, suppose that Diane states that Price is "moderately more important" than MPG. In this case, a numerical rating of 3 is assigned to the Price-MPG pairwise comparison. From Table 17.5, we see "strongly more important" receives a numerical rating of 5, while "very strongly more important" receives a numerical rating of 7. Intermediate judgments such as "strongly to very strongly more important" are possible and would receive a numerical rating of 6.

TABLE 17.5 COMPARISON SCALE FOR THE IMPORTANCE OF CRITERIA USING AHP

Verbal Judgment	Numerical Rating
Extremely more important	9
	8
Very strongly more important	7
	6
Strongly more important	5
	4
Moderately more important	3
	2
Equally important	1

Table 17.6 provides a summary of the six pairwise comparisons Diane provided for the car selection problem. Using the information in this table, Diane has specified that

> Price is moderately more important than MPG
>
> Price is equally to moderately more important than Comfort
>
> Price is equally to moderately more important than Style
>
> Comfort is moderately to strongly more important than MPG
>
> Style is moderately to strongly more important than MPG
>
> Style is equally to moderately more important than Comfort

AHP uses the numerical ratings from the pairwise comparisons to establish a priority or importance measure for each criterion.

As shown, the flexibility of AHP can accommodate the unique preferences of each individual decision maker. First, the choice of the criteria that are considered can vary depending upon the decision maker. Not everyone would agree that Price, MPG, Comfort, and Style are the only criteria to be considered in a car selection problem. Perhaps you would want to add safety, resale value, and/or other criteria if you were making the car selection decision. AHP can accommodate any set of criteria specified by the decision maker. Of course, if additional criteria are added, more pairwise comparisons will be necessary. In addition, if you agree with Diane that Price, MPG, Comfort, and Style are the four criteria to use, you would probably disagree with her as to the relative importance of the criteria. Using the format of Table 17.6, you could provide your own assessment of the importance of each pairwise comparison, and AHP would adjust the numerical ratings to reflect your personal preferences.

TABLE 17.6 SUMMARY OF DIANE PAYNE'S PAIRWISE COMPARISONS OF THE FOUR CRITERIA FOR THE CAR SELECTION PROBLEM

Pairwise Comparison	More Important Criterion	How Much More Important	Numerical Rating
Price-MPG	Price	Moderately	3
Price-Comfort	Price	Equally to moderately	2
Price-Style	Price	Equally to moderately	2
MPG-Comfort	Comfort	Moderately to strongly	4
MPG-Style	Style	Moderately to strongly	4
Comfort-Style	Style	Equally to moderately	2

Pairwise Comparison Matrix

To determine the priorities for the four criteria, we need to construct a matrix of the pairwise comparison ratings provided in Table 17.6. Using the four criteria, the **pairwise comparison matrix** will consist of four rows and four columns as shown here:

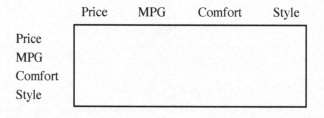

	Price	MPG	Comfort	Style
Price				
MPG				
Comfort				
Style				

Each of the numerical ratings in Table 17.6 must be entered into the pairwise comparison matrix. As an illustration of this process consider the numerical rating of 3 for the Price-MPG pairwise comparison. Table 17.6 shows that for this pairwise comparison that Price is the most important criterion. Thus, we must enter a 3 into the row labeled Price and the column labeled MPG in the pairwise comparison matrix. In general, the entries in the column labeled Most Important Criterion in Table 17.6 indicate which row of the pairwise comparison matrix the numerical rating must be placed in. As another illustration, consider the MPG-Comfort pairwise comparison. Table 17.6 shows that Comfort is the most important criterion for this pairwise comparison and that the numerical rating is 4. Thus, we enter a 4 into the row labeled Comfort and into the column labeled MPG. Following this procedure for the other pairwise comparisons shown in Table 17.6, we obtain the following pairwise comparison matrix.

	Price	MPG	Comfort	Style
Price		3	2	2
MPG				
Comfort		4		
Style		4	2	

Because the diagonal elements are comparing each criterion to itself, the diagonal elements of the pairwise comparison matrix are always equal to 1. For example, if Price is compared to Price, the verbal judgment would be "equally important" with a rating of 1; thus, a 1 would be placed into the row labeled Price and into the column labeled Price in the pairwise comparison matrix. At this point, the pairwise comparison matrix appears as follows:

	Price	MPG	Comfort	Style
Price	1	3	2	2
MPG		1		
Comfort		4	1	
Style		4	2	1

All that remains is to complete the entries for the remaining cells of the matrix. To illustrate how these values are obtained, consider the numerical rating of 3 for the Price-MPG pairwise comparison. This rating implies that the MPG-Price pairwise comparison should have a rating of ⅓. That is, because Diane already indicated Price is moderately more important than MPG (a rating of 3), we can infer that a pairwise comparison of MPG relative to Price should be ⅓. Similarly, because the Comfort-MPG pairwise comparison has a rating of 4, the MPG-Comfort pairwise comparison would be ¼. Thus, the complete pairwise comparison matrix for the car selection criteria is as follows:

	Price	MPG	Comfort	Style
Price	1	3	2	2
MPG	⅓	1	¼	¼
Comfort	½	4	1	½
Style	½	4	2	1

Synthesization

Using the pairwise comparison matrix, we can now calculate the priority of each criterion in terms of its contribution to the overall goal of selecting the best car. This aspect of AHP is referred to as **synthesization.** The exact mathematical procedure required to perform synthesization is beyond the scope of this text. However, the following three-step procedure provides a good approximation of the synthesization results.

1. Sum the values in each column of the pairwise comparison matrix.
2. Divide each element in the pairwise comparison matrix by its column total; the resulting matrix is referred to as the **normalized pairwise comparison matrix.**
3. Compute the average of the elements in each row of the normalized pairwise comparison matrix; these averages provide the priorities for the criteria.

To show how the synthesization process works, we carry out this three-step procedure for the criteria pairwise comparison matrix.

Step 1. Sum the values in each column.

	Price	MPG	Comfort	Style
Price	1	3	2	2
MPG	⅓	1	¼	¼
Comfort	½	4	1	½
Style	½	4	2	1
Sum	2.333	12.000	5.250	3.750

Step 2. Divide each element of the matrix by its column total.

	Price	MPG	Comfort	Style
Price	0.429	0.250	0.381	0.533
MPG	0.143	0.083	0.048	0.067
Comfort	0.214	0.333	0.190	0.133
Style	0.214	0.333	0.381	0.267

Step 3. Average the elements in each row to determine the priority of each criterion.

	Price	MPG	Comfort	Style	Priority
Price	0.429	0.250	0.381	0.533	0.398
MPG	0.143	0.083	0.048	0.067	0.085
Comfort	0.214	0.333	0.190	0.133	0.218
Style	0.214	0.333	0.381	0.267	0.299

The AHP synthesization procedure provides the priority of each criterion in terms of its contribution to the overall goal of selecting the best car. Thus, using Diane's pairwise comparisons provided in Table 17.6, AHP determines that Price with a priority of 0.398 is the most important criterion in the car selection process. Style with a priority of 0.299 ranks second in importance and is closely followed by Comfort with a priority of 0.218. MPG is the least important criterion with a priority of 0.085.

Consistency

A key step in AHP is the making of several pairwise comparisons as previously described. An important consideration in this process is the **consistency** of the pairwise judgments provided by the decision maker. For example, if criterion A compared to criterion B has a numerical rating of 3 and if criterion B compared to criterion C has a numerical rating of 2, perfect consistency of criterion A compared to criterion C would have a numerical rating of $3 \times 2 = 6$. If the A to C numerical rating assigned by the decision maker was 4 or 5, some inconsistency would exist among the pairwise comparison.

With numerous pairwise comparisons, perfect consistency is difficult to achieve. In fact, some degree of inconsistency can be expected to exist in almost any set of pairwise comparisons. To handle the consistency issue, AHP provides a method for measuring the degree of consistency among the pairwise comparisons provided by the decision maker. If the degree of consistency is unacceptable, the decision maker should review and revise the pairwise comparisons before proceeding with the AHP analysis.

AHP provides a measure of the consistency for the pairwise comparisons by computing a **consistency ratio.** This ratio is designed in such a way that a value *greater than* 0.10 indicates an inconsistency in the pairwise judgments. Thus, if the consistency ratio is 0.10 or less, the consistency of the pairwise comparisons is considered reasonable, and the AHP process can continue with the synthesization computations.

Although the exact mathematical computation of the consistency ratio is beyond the scope of this text, an approximation of the ratio can be obtained with little difficulty. The

A consistency ratio greater than 0.10 indicates inconsistency in the pairwise comparisons. In such cases, the decision maker should review the pairwise comparisons before proceeding.

step-by-step procedure for estimating the consistency ratio for the criteria of the car selection problem follows.

Step 1. Multiply each value in the first column of the pairwise comparison matrix by the priority of the first item; multiply each value in the second column of the pairwise comparison matrix by the priority of the second item; continue this process for all columns of the pairwise comparison matrix. Sum the values across the rows to obtain a vector of values labeled "weighted sum." This computation for the car selection problem is as follows:

$$0.398\begin{bmatrix}1\\ \frac{1}{3}\\ \frac{1}{2}\\ \frac{1}{2}\end{bmatrix} + 0.085\begin{bmatrix}3\\1\\4\\4\end{bmatrix} + 0.218\begin{bmatrix}2\\ \frac{1}{2}\\1\\2\end{bmatrix} + 0.299\begin{bmatrix}2\\ \frac{1}{4}\\ \frac{1}{2}\\1\end{bmatrix} =$$

$$\begin{bmatrix}0.398\\0.133\\0.199\\0.199\end{bmatrix} + \begin{bmatrix}0.255\\0.085\\0.340\\0.340\end{bmatrix} + \begin{bmatrix}0.436\\0.054\\0.218\\0.436\end{bmatrix} + \begin{bmatrix}0.598\\0.075\\0.149\\0.299\end{bmatrix} = \begin{bmatrix}1.687\\0.347\\0.907\\1.274\end{bmatrix}$$

Step 2. Divide the elements of the weighted sum vector obtained in step 1 by the corresponding priority for each criterion.

Price $\quad \dfrac{1.687}{0.398} = 4.236$

MPG $\quad \dfrac{0.347}{0.085} = 4.077$

Comfort $\quad \dfrac{0.907}{0.218} = 4.163$

Style $\quad \dfrac{1.274}{0.299} = 4.264$

Step 3. Compute the average of the values found in step 2; this average is denoted λ_{max}.

$$\lambda_{max} = \frac{(4.236 + 4.077 + 4.163 + 4.264)}{4} = 4.185$$

Step 4. Compute the consistency index (CI) as follows:

$$CI = \frac{\lambda_{max} - n}{n - 1}$$

where n is the number of items being compared. Thus, we have

$$CI = \frac{4.185 - 4}{4 - 1} = 0.0616$$

Step 5. Compute the consistency ratio, which is defined as

$$CR = \frac{CI}{RI}$$

where RI is the consistency index of a *randomly* generated pairwise comparison matrix. The value of RI depends on the number of items being compared and is given as follows:

n	3	4	5	6	7	8
RI	0.58	0.90	1.12	1.24	1.32	1.41

Thus, for the car selection problem with $n = 4$ criteria, we have RI = 0.90 and a consistency ratio

$$\text{CR} = \frac{0.0616}{0.90} = 0.068$$

Problem 16 will give you practice with the synthesization calculations and determining the consistency ratio.

As mentioned previously, a consistency ratio of 0.10 or less is considered acceptable. Because the pairwise comparisons for the car selection criteria show CR = 0.068, we can conclude that the degree of consistency in the pairwise comparisons is acceptable.

Other Pairwise Comparisons for the Car Selection Problem

Continuing with the AHP analysis of the car selection problem, we need to use the pairwise comparison procedure to determine the priorities for the three cars using each of the criteria: Price, MPG, Comfort, and Style. Determining these priorities requires Diane to express pairwise comparison preferences for the cars using each criterion one at a time. For example, using the Price criterion, Diane must make the following pairwise comparisons:

the Accord compared to the Saturn

the Accord compared to the Cavalier

the Saturn compared to the Cavalier

In each comparison, Diane must select the more preferred car and then express a judgment of how much more preferred the selected car is.

For example, using the Price as the basis for comparison, assume that Diane considers the Accord-Saturn pairwise comparison and indicates that the less expensive Saturn is preferred. Table 17.7 shows how AHP uses Diane's verbal description of the preference between the Accord and Saturn to determine a numerical rating of the preference. For

TABLE 17.7   PAIRWISE COMPARISON SCALE FOR THE PREFERENCE OF DECISION ALTERNATIVES USING AHP

Verbal Judgment	Numerical Rating
Extremely preferred	9
	8
Very strongly preferred	7
	6
Strongly preferred	5
	4
Moderately preferred	3
	2
Equally preferred	1

TABLE 17.8 PAIRWISE COMPARISON MATRIXES SHOWING PREFERENCES FOR THE CARS USING EACH CRITERION

Price

	Accord	Saturn	Cavalier
Accord	1	$\frac{1}{3}$	$\frac{1}{4}$
Saturn	3	1	$\frac{1}{2}$
Cavalier	4	2	1

MPG

	Accord	Saturn	Cavalier
Accord	1	$\frac{1}{4}$	$\frac{1}{6}$
Saturn	4	1	$\frac{1}{3}$
Cavalier	6	3	1

Comfort

	Accord	Saturn	Cavalier
Accord	1	2	8
Saturn	$\frac{1}{2}$	1	6
Cavalier	$\frac{1}{8}$	$\frac{1}{6}$	1

Style

	Accord	Saturn	Cavalier
Accord	1	$\frac{1}{3}$	4
Saturn	3	1	7
Cavalier	$\frac{1}{4}$	$\frac{1}{7}$	1

example, suppose that Diane states that based on Price, the Saturn is "moderately more preferred" to the Accord. Thus, using the Price criterion, a numerical rating of 3 is assigned to the Saturn row and Accord column of the pairwise comparison matrix.

Table 17.8 shows the summary of the car pairwise comparisons that Diane provided for each criterion of the car selection problem. Using this table and referring to selected pairwise comparison entries, we see that Diane stated the following preferences:

In terms of Price, the Cavalier is moderately to strongly more preferred than the Accord.

In terms of MPG, the Cavalier is moderately more preferred than the Saturn.

In terms of Comfort, the Accord is very strongly to extremely more preferred than the Cavalier.

In terms of Style, the Saturn is moderately more preferred than the Accord.

Using the pairwise comparison matrixes in Table 17.8, many other insights may be gained about the preferences Diana expressed for the cars. However, at this point, AHP continues by synthesizing each of the four pairwise comparison matrixes in Table 17.8 in order to determine the priority of each car using each criterion. A synthesization is conducted for each pairwise comparison matrix using the three-step procedure described previously for the criteria pairwise comparison matrix. Four synthesization computations provide the four sets of priorities shown in Table 17.9. Using this table, we see that the

Practice setting up a pairwise comparison matrix and determine whether judgments are consistent by working Problem 20.

TABLE 17.9 PRIORITIES FOR EACH CAR USING EACH CRITERION

	Criterion			
	Price	MPG	Comfort	Style
Accord	0.123	0.087	0.593	0.265
Saturn	0.320	0.274	0.341	0.656
Cavalier	0.557	0.639	0.065	0.080

Cavalier is the preferred alternative based on Price (0.557), the Cavalier is the preferred alternative based on MPG (0.639), the Accord is the preferred alternative based on Comfort (0.593), and the Saturn is the preferred alternative based on Style (0.656). At this point, no car is the clear, overall best. The next section shows how to combine the priorities for the criteria and the priorities in Table 17.9 to develop an overall priority ranking for the three cars.

17.6   USING AHP TO DEVELOP AN OVERALL PRIORITY RANKING

In Section 17.5, we used Diane's pairwise comparisons of the four criteria to develop the priorities of 0.398 for Price, 0.085 for MPG, 0.218 for Comfort, and 0.299 for Style. We now want to use these priorities and the priorities shown in Table 17.9 to develop an overall priority ranking for the three cars.

The procedure used to compute the overall priority is to weight each car's priority shown in Table 17.9 by the corresponding criterion priority. For example, the Price criterion has a priority of 0.398, and the Accord has a priority of 0.123 in terms of the Price criterion. Thus, $0.398 \times 0.123 = 0.049$ is the priority value of the Accord based on the Price criterion. To obtain the overall priority of the Accord, we need to make similar computations for the MPG, Comfort, and Style criteria and then add the values to obtain the overall priority. This calculation is as follows:

Overall Priority of the Accord:

$$0.398(0.123) + 0.085(0.087) + 0.218(0.593) + 0.299(0.265) = 0.265$$

Repeating this calculation for the Saturn and the Cavalier, we obtain the following results:

Overall Priority of the Saturn:

$$0.398(0.320) + 0.085(0.274) + 0.218(0.341) + 0.299(0.656) = 0.421$$

Overall Priority of the Cavalier:

$$0.398(0.557) + 0.085(0.639) + 0.218(0.065) + 0.299(0.080) = 0.314$$

Ranking these priorities, we have the AHP ranking of the decision alternatives:

Car	Priority
1. Saturn	0.421
2. Cavalier	0.314
3. Accord	0.265

Work Problem 24 and determine the AHP priorities for two decision alternatives.

These results provide a basis for Diane to make a decision regarding the purchase of a car. As long as Diane believes that her judgments regarding the importance of the criteria and her preferences for the cars using each criterion are valid, the AHP priorities show that the Saturn is preferred. In addition to the recommendation of the Saturn as the best car, the AHP analysis helped Diane gain a better understanding of the trade-offs in the decision-making process and a clearer understanding of why the Saturn is the AHP recommended alternative.

NOTES AND COMMENTS

1. The scoring model in Section 17.3 used the following equation to compute the overall score of a decision alternative.

$$S_j = \sum_i w_i \, r_{ij}$$

   where

   w_i = the weight for criterion i

   r_{ij} = the rating for criterion i and decision alternative j

   In this section AHP used the same calculation to determine the overall priority of each decision alternative. The difference between the two approaches is that the scoring model required the decision maker to estimate the values of w_i and r_{ij} directly. AHP used synthesization to compute the criterion priorities w_i and the decision alternative priorities r_{ij} based on the pairwise comparison information provided by the decision maker.

2. The software package Expert Choice® marketed by Decision Support Software provides a user-friendly procedure for implementing AHP on a personal computer. Expert Choice takes the decision maker through the pairwise comparison process in a step-by-step manner. Once the decision maker responds to the pairwise comparison prompts, Expert Choice automatically constructs the pairwise comparison matrix, conducts the synthesization calculations, and presents the overall priorities. Expert Choice is a software package that should warrant consideration by a decision maker who anticipates solving a variety of multicriteria decision problems.

SUMMARY

In this chapter we used goal programming to solve problems with multiple goals within the linear programming framework. We showed that the goal programming model contains one or more goal equations and an objective function designed to minimize deviations from the goals. In situations where resource capacities or other restrictions affect the achievement of the goals, the model will contain constraints that are formulated and treated in the same manner as constraints in an ordinary linear programming model.

In goal programming problems with preemptive priorities, priority level 1 goals are treated first in an objective function to identify a solution that will best satisfy these goals. This solution is then revised by considering an objective function involving only the priority level 2 goals; solution modifications are considered only if they do not degrade the solution obtained for the priority level 1 goals. This process continues until all priority levels have been considered.

We showed how a variation of the linear programming graphical solution procedure can be used to solve goal programming problems with two decision variables. Specialized goal programming computer packages are available for solving the general goal programming problem, but such computer codes are not as readily available as are general purpose linear programming computer packages. As a result, we showed how the linear programming module of The Management Scientist software package can be used to solve a goal programming problem.

We then presented a scoring model as a quick and relatively easy way to identify the most desired decision alternative in a multicriteria problem. The decision maker provides a subjective weight indicating the importance of each criterion. Then the decision maker rates each decision alternative in terms of how well it satisfies each criterion. The end result is a score for each decision alternative that indicates the preference for the decision alternative considering all criteria.

We also presented an approach to multicriteria decision making called the analytic hierarchy process (AHP). We showed that a key part of AHP is the development of judgments concerning the relative importance of, or preference for, the elements being compared. A consistency ratio is computed to determine the degree of consistency exhibited by the decision maker in making the pairwise comparisons. Values of the consistency ratio less than or equal to 0.10 are considered acceptable.

Once the set of all pairwise comparisons has been developed, a process referred to as synthesization is used to determine the priorities for the elements being compared. The final step of the analytic hierarchy process involves multiplying the priority levels established for the decision alternatives relative to each criterion by the priority levels reflecting the importance of the criteria themselves; the sum of these products over all the criteria provides the overall priority level for each decision alternative.

GLOSSARY

Goal programming   A linear programming approach to multicriteria decision problems whereby the objective function is designed to minimize the deviations from goals.

Preemptive priorities   Priorities assigned to goals that ensure that the satisfaction of a higher level goal cannot be traded for the satisfaction of a lower level goal.

Target value   A value specified in the statement of the goal. Based on the context of the problem, management will want the solution to the goal programming problem to result in a value for the goal that is less than, equal to, or greater than the target value.

Goal equation   An equation whose right-hand side is the target value for the goal; the left-hand side of the goal equation consists of (1) a function representing the level of achievement and (2) deviation variables representing the difference between the target value for the goal and the level achieved.

Deviation variables   Variables that are added to the goal equation to allow the solution to deviate from the goal's target value.

Scoring model   An approach to multicriteria decision making that requires the user to assign weights to each criterion that describes the criterion's relative importance and to assign a rating that shows how well each decision alternative satisfies each criterion. The output is a score for each decision alternative.

Analytic hierarchy process (AHP)   An approach to multicriteria decision making based on pairwise comparisons for elements in a hierarchy.

Hierarchy   A diagram that shows the levels of a problem in terms of the overall goal, the criteria, and the decision alternatives.

Pairwise comparison matrix   A matrix that consists of the preference, or relative importance, ratings provided during a series of pairwise comparisons.

Synthesization   A mathematical process that uses the preference or relative importance values in the pairwise comparison matrix to develop priorities.

Normalized pairwise comparison matrix   The matrix obtained by dividing each element of the pairwise comparison matrix by its column total. This matrix is computed as an intermediate step in the synthesization of priorities.

Consistency   A concept developed to assess the quality of the judgments made during a series of pairwise comparisons. It is a measure of the internal consistency of these comparisons.

Consistency ratio   A numerical measure of the degree of consistency in a series of pairwise comparisons. Values less than or equal to 0.10 are considered reasonable.

PROBLEMS

1. The RMC Corporation blends three raw materials to produce two products: a fuel additive and a solvent base. Each ton of fuel additive is a mixture of $\frac{2}{5}$ ton of material 1 and $\frac{3}{5}$ ton of material 3. A ton of solvent base is a mixture of $\frac{1}{2}$ ton of material 1, $\frac{1}{5}$ ton of material 2, and $\frac{3}{10}$ ton of material 3. RMC's production is constrained by a limited availability of the

three raw materials. For the current production period, RMC has the following quantities of each raw material: material 1, 20 tons; material 2, 5 tons; material 3, 21 tons. Management wants to achieve the following P_1 priority level goals.

Goal 1: Produce at least 30 tons of fuel additive.

Goal 2: Produce at least 15 tons of solvent base.

Assume there are no other goals.
a. Is it possible for management to achieve both P_1 level goals given the constraints on the amounts of each material available? Explain.
b. Treating the amounts of each material available as constraints, formulate a goal programming model to determine the optimal product mix. Assume that both P_1 priority level goals are equally important to management.
c. Use the graphical goal programming procedure to solve the model formulated in part (b).
d. If goal 1 is twice as important as goal 2, what is the optimal product mix?

2. DJS Investment Services must develop an investment portfolio for a new client. As an initial investment strategy, the new client would like to restrict the portfolio to a mix of two stocks:

Stock	Price/Share ($)	Estimated Annual Return (%)
AGA Products	50	6
Key Oil	100	10

The client wants to invest $50,000 and established the following two investment goals.

Priority Level 1 Goal

Goal 1: Obtain an annual return of at least 9%.

Priority Level 2 Goal

Goal 2: Limit the investment in Key Oil, the riskier investment, to no more than 60% of the total investment.
a. Formulate a goal programming model for the DJS Investment problem.
b. Use the graphical goal programming procedure to obtain a solution.

3. The L. Young & Sons Manufacturing Company produces two products, which have the following profit and resource requirement characteristics.

Characteristic	Product 1	Product 2
Profit/unit	$4	$2
Dept. A hours/unit	1	1
Dept. B hours/unit	2	5

Last month's production schedule used 350 hours of labor in department A and 1000 hours of labor in department B.

Young's management has been experiencing workforce morale and labor union problems during the past six months because of monthly departmental workload fluctuations. New hiring, layoffs, and interdepartmental transfers have been common because the firm has not attempted to stabilize workload requirements.

Management would like to develop a production schedule for the coming month that will achieve the following goals.

Goal 1: Use 350 hours of labor in department A.

Goal 2: Use 1000 hours of labor in department B.

Goal 3: Earn a profit of at least $1300.

a. Formulate a goal programming model for this problem, assuming that goals 1 and 2 are P_1 level goals and goal 3 is a P_2 level goal; assume that goals 1 and 2 are equally important.

b. Solve the model formulated in part (a) using the graphical goal programming procedure.

c. Suppose that the firm ignores the workload fluctuations and considers the 350 hours in department A and the 1000 hours in department B as the maximum available. Formulate and solve a linear programming problem to maximize profit subject to these constraints.

d. Compare the solutions obtained in parts (b) and (c). Discuss which approach you favor, and why.

e. Reconsider part (a) assuming that the priority level 1 goal is goal 3 and the priority level 2 goals are goals 1 and 2; as before, assume that goals 1 and 2 are equally important. Solve this revised problem using the graphical goal programming procedure and compare your solution to the one obtained for the original problem.

4. Industrial Chemicals produces two adhesives used in the manufacturing process for airplanes. The two adhesives, which have different bonding strengths, require different amounts of production time: the IC-100 adhesive requires 20 minutes of production time per gallon of finished product, and the IC-200 adhesive uses 30 minutes of production time per gallon. Both products use 1 pound of a highly perishable resin for each gallon of finished product. Inventory currently holds 300 pounds of the resin, and more can be obtained if necessary. However, because of the shelf life of the material, any amount not used in the next two weeks will be discarded.

The firm has existing orders for 100 gallons of IC-100 and 120 gallons of IC-200. Under normal conditions, the production process operates eight hours per day, five days per week. Management wants to schedule production for the next two weeks to achieve the following goals.

Priority Level 1 Goals

Goal 1: Avoid underutilization of the production process.

Goal 2: Avoid overtime in excess of 20 hours for the two weeks.

Priority Level 2 Goals

Goal 3: Satisfy existing orders for the IC-100 adhesive; that is, produce at least 100 gallons of IC-100.

Goal 4: Satisfy existing orders for the IC-200 adhesive; that is, produce at least 120 gallons of IC-200.

Priority Level 3 Goal

Goal 5: Use all the available resin.

a. Formulate a goal programming model for the Industrial Chemicals problem. Assume that both priority level 1 goals and that both priority level 2 goals are equally important.

b. Use the graphical goal programming procedure to develop a solution for the model formulated in part (a).

5. Standard Pump recently won a $14 million contract with the U.S. Navy to supply 2000 custom-designed submersible pumps over the next four months. The contract calls for the delivery of 200 pumps at the end of May, 600 pumps at the end of June, 600 pumps at the end of July, and 600 pumps at the end of August. Standard's production capacity is 500 pumps in May, 400 pumps in June, 800 pumps in July, and 500 pumps in August. Management would like to develop a production schedule that will keep monthly ending inventories low while at the same time minimizing the fluctuations in inventory levels from month to month. In attempting to develop a goal programming model of the problem, the company's production scheduler let x_m denote the number of pumps produced in month m and s_m denote the number of pumps in inventory at the end of month m. Here, $m = 1$ refers to May, $m = 2$ refers to June, $m = 3$ refers to July, and $m = 4$ refers to August. Management asks you to assist the production scheduler in model development.

  a. Using these variables, develop a constraint for each month that will satisfy the following demand requirement:

$$\begin{pmatrix} \text{Beginning} \\ \text{Inventory} \end{pmatrix} + \begin{pmatrix} \text{Current} \\ \text{Production} \end{pmatrix} - \begin{pmatrix} \text{Ending} \\ \text{Inventory} \end{pmatrix} = \begin{pmatrix} \text{This Month's} \\ \text{Demand} \end{pmatrix}$$

  b. Write goal equations that represent the fluctuations in the production level from May to June, June to July, and July to August.

  c. Inventory carrying costs are high. Is it possible for Standard to avoid carrying any monthly ending inventories over the scheduling period of May to August? If not, develop goal equations with a target of zero for the ending inventory in May, June, and July.

  d. Besides the goal equations developed in parts (b) and (c), what other constraints are needed in the model?

  e. Assuming the production fluctuation and inventory goals are of equal importance, develop and solve a goal programming model to determine the best production schedule.

  f. Can you find a way to reduce the variables and constraints needed in your model by eliminating the goal equations and deviation variables for ending inventory levels? Explain.

6. Michigan Motors Corporation (MMC) just introduced a new luxury touring sedan. As part of its promotional campaign, the marketing department decided to send personalized invitations to test drive the new sedan to two target groups: (1) current owners of an MMC luxury automobile and (2) owners of luxury cars manufactured by one of MMC's competitors. The cost of sending a personalized invitation to each customer is estimated to be $1 per letter. Based on previous experience with this type of advertising, MMC estimates that 25% of the customers contacted from group 1 and 10% of the customers contacted from group 2 will test drive the new sedan. As part of this campaign, MMC set the following goals.

Goal 1: Get at least 10,000 customers from group 1 to test drive the new sedan.

Goal 2: Get at least 5000 customers from group 2 to test drive the new sedan.

Goal 3: Limit the expense of sending out the invitations to $70,000.

Assume that goals 1 and 2 are P_1 priority level goals and that goal 3 is a P_2 priority level goal.

  a. Suppose that goals 1 and 2 are equally important; formulate a goal programming model of the MMC problem.

  b. Use the goal programming computer procedure illustrated in Section 17.2 to solve the model formulated in part (a).

  c. If management believes that contacting customers from group 2 is twice as important as contacting customers from group 1, what should MMC do?

7. A committee in charge of promoting a Ladies Professional Golf Association tournament is trying to determine how best to advertise the event during the two weeks prior to the tournament. The committee obtained the following information about the three advertising media they are considering using.

Category	Audience Reached per Advertisement	Cost per Advertisement	Maximum Number of Advertisements
TV	200,000	$2500	10
Radio	50,000	$ 400	15
Newspaper	100,000	$ 500	20

The last column in this table shows the maximum number of advertisements that can be run during the next two weeks; these values should be treated as constraints. The committee established the following goals for the campaign.

Priority Level 1 Goal

Goal 1:   Reach at least 4 million people.

Priority Level 2 Goal

Goal 2:   The number of television advertisements should be at least 30% of the total number of advertisements.

Priority Level 3 Goal

Goal 3:   The number of radio advertisements should not exceed 20% of the total number of advertisements.

Priority Level 4 Goal

Goal 4:   Limit the total amount spent for advertising to $20,000.

   a.   Formulate a goal programming model for this problem.
   b.   Use the goal programming computer procedure illustrated in Section 17.2 to solve the model formulated in part (a).

8. Morley Company is attempting to determine the best location for a new machine in an existing layout of three machines. The existing machines are located at the following x_1, x_2 coordinates on the shop floor.

$$\begin{aligned}
\text{Machine 1:} \quad & x_1 = 1, x_2 = 7 \\
\text{Machine 2:} \quad & x_1 = 5, x_2 = 9 \\
\text{Machine 3:} \quad & x_1 = 6, x_2 = 2
\end{aligned}$$

   a.   Develop a goal programming model that can be solved to minimize the total distance of the new machine from the three existing machines. The distance is to be measured rectangularly. For example, if the location of the new machine is $(x_1 = 3, x_2 = 5)$, it is considered to be a distance of $|3 - 1| + |5 - 7| = 2 + 2 = 4$ from machine 1. *Hint:* In the goal programming formulation, let

$$\begin{aligned}
x_1 =\ & \text{first coordinate of the new machine location} \\
x_2 =\ & \text{second coordinate of the new machine location} \\
d_i^+ =\ & \text{amount by which the } x_1 \text{ coordinate of the new machine} \\
& \text{exceeds the } x_1 \text{ coordinate of machine } i\ (i = 1, 2, 3) \\
d_i^- =\ & \text{amount by which the } x_1 \text{ coordinate of machine } i \\
& \text{exceeds the } x_1 \text{ coordinate of the new machine } (i = 1, 2, 3) \\
e_i^+ =\ & \text{amount by which the } x_2 \text{ coordinate of the new machine} \\
& \text{exceeds the } x_2 \text{ coordinate of machine } i\ (i = 1, 2, 3) \\
e_i^- =\ & \text{amount by which the } x_2 \text{ coordinate of machine } i \\
& \text{exceeds the } x_2 \text{ coordinate of the new machine } (i = 1, 2, 3)
\end{aligned}$$

   b.   What is the optimal location for the new machine?

9. One advantage of using the multicriteria decision-making methods presented in this chapter is that the criteria weights and the decision alternative ratings may be modified to reflect the unique interests and preferences of each individual decision maker. For example, assume that another graduating college student had the same three job offers described in Section 17.3. This student provided the following scoring model information. Rank the overall preference for the three positions. Which position is recommended?

Criteria	Weight	Ratings		
		Analyst Chicago	Accountant Denver	Auditor Houston
Career advancement	5	7	4	4
Location	2	5	6	4
Management style	5	6	5	7
Salary	4	7	8	4
Prestige	4	8	5	6
Job security	2	4	5	8
Enjoyment of the work	4	7	5	5

10. The Kenyon Manufacturing Company is interested in selecting the best location for a new plant. After a detailed study of 10 sites, the three location finalists are Georgetown, Kentucky; Marysville, Ohio; and Clarksville, Tennessee. The Kenyon management team provided the following data on location criteria, criteria importance, and location ratings. Use a scoring model to determine the best location for the new plant.

Criteria	Weight	Ratings		
		Georgetown, Kentucky	Marysville, Ohio	Clarksville, Tennessee
Land cost	4	7	4	5
Labor cost	3	6	5	8
Labor availability	5	7	8	6
Construction cost	4	6	7	5
Transportation	3	5	7	4
Access to customers	5	6	8	5
Long-range goals	4	7	6	5

11. The Davis family of Atlanta, Georgia, is planning its annual summer vacation. Three vacation locations along with criteria weights and location ratings follow. What is the recommended vacation location?

Criteria	Weight	Ratings		
		Myrtle Beach, South Carolina	Smoky Mountains	Branson, Missouri
Travel distance	2	5	7	3
Vacation cost	5	5	6	4
Entertainment available	3	7	4	8
Outdoor activities	2	9	6	5
Unique experience	4	6	7	8
Family fun	5	8	7	7

12. A high school senior is considering attending one of the following four colleges or universities. Eight criteria, criteria weights, and school ratings are also shown. What is the recommended choice?

Criteria	Weight	Ratings			
		Midwestern University	State College at Newport	Handover College	Tecumseh State
School prestige	3	8	6	7	5
Number of students	4	3	5	8	7
Average class size	5	4	5	8	7
Cost	5	5	8	3	6
Distance from home	2	7	8	7	6
Sports program	4	9	5	4	6
Housing desirability	4	6	5	7	6
Beauty of campus	3	5	3	8	5

13. Mr. and Mrs. Brinkley are interested in purchasing condominium property in Naples, Florida. The three most preferred condominiums are listed along with criteria weights and rating information. Which condominium is preferred?

Criteria	Weight	Ratings		
		Park Shore	The Terrace	Gulf View
Cost	5	5	6	5
Location	4	7	4	9
Appearance	5	7	4	7
Parking	2	5	8	5
Floor plan	4	8	7	5
Swimming pool	1	7	2	3
View	3	5	4	9
Kitchen	4	8	7	6
Closet space	3	6	8	4

14. Clark and Julie Anderson are interested in purchasing a new boat and have limited their choice to one of three boats manufactured by Sea Ray, Inc.: the 220 Bowrider, the 230 Overnighter, and the 240 Sundancer. The Bowrider weighs 3100 pounds, has no overnight capability, and has a price of $28,500. The 230 Overnighter weighs 4300 pounds, has a reasonable overnight capability, and has a price of $37,500. The 240 Sundancer weighs 4500 pounds, has an excellent overnight capability (kitchen, bath, and bed), and has a price of $48,200. The Andersons provided the scoring model information separately as shown here.

Clark Anderson

Criteria	Weight	Ratings		
		220 Bowrider	230 Overnighter	240 Sundancer
Cost	5	8	5	3
Overnight capability	3	2	6	9
Kitchen/bath facilities	2	1	4	7
Appearance	5	7	7	6
Engine/speed	5	6	8	4
Towing/handling	4	8	5	2
Maintenance	4	7	5	3
Resale value	3	7	5	6

Julie Anderson

Criteria	Weight	Ratings 220 Bowrider	230 Overnighter	240 Sundancer
Cost	3	7	6	5
Overnight capability	5	1	6	8
Kitchen/bath facilities	5	1	3	7
Appearance	4	5	7	7
Engine/speed	2	4	5	3
Towing/handling	2	8	6	2
Maintenance	1	6	5	4
Resale value	2	5	6	6

    a. Which boat does Clark Anderson prefer?
    b. Which boat does Julie Anderson prefer?

15. Use the pairwise comparison matrix for the price criterion shown in Table 17.8 to verify that the priorities after synthesization are 0.123, 0.320, and 0.557. Compute the consistency ratio and comment on its acceptability.

16. Use the pairwise comparison matrix for the style criterion as shown in Table 17.8 to verify that the priorities after synthesization are 0.265, 0.656, and 0.080. Compute the consistency ratio and comment on its acceptability.

17. Dan Joseph was considering entering one of two graduate schools of business to pursue studies for an MBA degree. When asked how he compared the two schools with respect to reputation, he responded that he preferred school A strongly to very strongly to school B.
    a. Set up the pairwise comparison matrix for this problem.
    b. Determine the priorities for the two schools relative to this criterion.

18. An organization was investigating relocating its corporate headquarters to one of three possible cities. The following pairwise comparison matrix shows the president's judgments regarding the desirability for the three cities.

	City 1	City 2	City 3
City 1	1	5	7
City 2	1/5	1	3
City 3	1/7	1/3	1

    a. Determine the priorities for the three cities.
    b. Is the president consistent in terms of the judgments provided? Explain.

19. The following pairwise comparison matrix contains the judgments of an individual regarding the fairness of two proposed tax programs, A and B.

	A	B
A	1	3
B	1/3	1

    a. Determine the priorities for the two programs.
    b. Are the individual's judgments consistent? Explain.

20. Asked to compare three soft drinks with respect to flavor, an individual stated that

> A is moderately more preferable than B.
>
> A is equally to moderately more preferable than C.
>
> B is strongly more preferable than C.

  a. Set up the pairwise comparison matrix for this problem.
  b. Determine the priorities for the soft drinks with respect to the flavor criterion.
  c. Compute the consistency ratio. Are the individual's judgments consistent? Explain.

21. Refer to Problem 20. Suppose that the individual had stated the following judgments instead of those given in Problem 20.

> A is strongly more preferable than C.
>
> B is equally to moderately more preferable than A.
>
> B is strongly more preferable than C.

Answer parts (a), (b), and (c) as stated in Problem 20.

22. The national sales director for Jones Office Supplies needs to determine the best location for the next national sales meeting. Three locations have been proposed: Dallas, San Francisco, and New York. One criterion considered important in the decision is the desirability of the location in terms of restaurants, entertainment, and so on. The national sales manager made the following judgments with regard to this criterion.

> New York is very strongly more preferred than Dallas.
>
> New York is moderately more preferred than San Francisco.
>
> San Francisco is moderately to strongly more preferred than Dallas.

  a. Set up the pairwise comparison matrix for this problem.
  b. Determine the priorities for the desirability criterion.
  c. Compute the consistency ratio. Are the sales manager's judgments consistent? Explain.

23. A study comparing four personal computers resulted in the following pairwise comparison matrix for the performance criterion.

	1	2	3	4
1	1	3	7	$\frac{1}{3}$
2	$\frac{1}{3}$	1	4	$\frac{1}{4}$
3	$\frac{1}{7}$	$\frac{1}{4}$	1	$\frac{1}{6}$
4	3	4	6	1

  a. Determine the priorities for the four computers relative to the performance criterion.
  b. Compute the consistency ratio. Are the judgments regarding performance consistent? Explain.

24. An individual was interested in determining which of two stocks to invest in, Central Computing Company (CCC) or Software Research, Inc. (SRI). The criteria thought to be most relevant in making the decision are the potential yield of the stock and the risk associated with the investment. The pairwise comparison matrixes for this problem are

Criterion	Yield	Risk		Yield	CCC	SRI		Risk	CCC	SRI
Yield	1	2		**CCC**	1	3		**CCC**	1	$\frac{1}{2}$
Risk	$\frac{1}{2}$	1		**SRI**	$\frac{1}{3}$	1		**SRI**	2	1

a. Compute the priorities for each pairwise comparison matrix.
b. Determine the overall priority for the two investments, CCC and SRI. Which investment is preferred based on yield and risk?

25. The vice president of Harling Equipment needs to select a new director of marketing. The two possible candidates are Bill Jacobs and Sue Martin, and the criteria thought to be most relevant in the selection are leadership ability (L), personal skills (P), and administrative skills (A). The following pairwise comparison matrixes were obtained.

Criterion	L	P	A
L	1	$\frac{1}{3}$	$\frac{1}{4}$
P	3	1	2
A	4	$\frac{1}{2}$	1

Leadership	Jacobs	Martin
Jacobs	1	4
Martin	$\frac{1}{4}$	1

Personal	Jacobs	Martin
Jacobs	1	$\frac{1}{3}$
Martin	3	1

Administrative	Jacobs	Martin
Jacobs	1	2
Martin	$\frac{1}{2}$	1

a. Compute the priorities for each pairwise comparison matrix.
b. Determine an overall priority for each candidate. Which candidate is preferred?

26. A woman considering the purchase of a custom sound stereo system for her car looked at three different systems (A, B, and C), which varied in terms of price, sound quality, and FM reception. The following pairwise comparison matrixes were developed.

Criterion	Price	Sound	Reception
Price	1	3	4
Sound	$\frac{1}{3}$	1	3
Reception	$\frac{1}{4}$	$\frac{1}{3}$	1

Price	A	B	C
A	1	4	2
B	$\frac{1}{4}$	1	$\frac{1}{3}$
C	$\frac{1}{2}$	3	1

Sound	A	B	C
A	1	$\frac{1}{2}$	$\frac{1}{4}$
B	2	1	$\frac{1}{3}$
C	4	3	1

Reception	A	B	C
A	1	4	2
B	$\frac{1}{4}$	1	1
C	$\frac{1}{2}$	1	1

a. Compute the priorities for each pairwise comparison matrix.
b. Determine an overall priority for each system. Which stereo system is preferred?

Case Problem   EZ TRAILERS, INC.

EZ Trailers, Inc., manufactures a variety of general purpose trailers, including a complete line of boat trailers. Two of their best-selling boat trailers are the EZ-190 and the EZ-250. The EZ-190 is designed for boats up to 19 feet in length, and the EZ-250 can be used for boats up to 25 feet in length.

EZ Trailers would like to schedule production for the next two months for these two models. Each unit of the EZ-190 requires four hours of production time, and each unit of the EZ-250 uses six hours of production time. The following orders have been received for March and April.

Model	March	April
EZ-190	800	600
EZ-250	1100	1200

The ending inventory from February was 200 units of the EZ-190 and 300 units of the EZ-250. The total number of hours of production time used in February was 6300 hours.

The management of EZ Trailers is concerned about being able to satisfy existing orders for the EZ-250 for both March and April. In fact, it believes that this goal is the most important one that a production schedule should meet. Next in importance is satisfying existing orders for the EZ-190. In addition, management doesn't want to implement any production schedule that would involve significant labor fluctuations from month to month. In this regard, its goal is to develop a production schedule that would limit fluctuations in labor hours used to a maximum of 1000 hours from one month to the next.

Managerial Report

Perform an analysis of EZ Trailers's production scheduling problem, and prepare a report for EZ's president that summarizes your findings. Include a discussion and analysis of the following items in your report.

1. The production schedule that best achieves the goals as specified by management.
2. Suppose that EZ Trailers's storage facilities would accommodate only a maximum of 300 trailers in any one month. What effect would this have on the production schedule?
3. Suppose that EZ Trailers can store only a maximum of 300 trailers in any one month. In addition, suppose management would like to have an ending inventory in April of at least 100 units of each model. What effect would both changes have on the production schedule?
4. What changes would occur in the production schedule if the labor fluctuation goal was the highest priority goal?

Appendix 17.1   SCORING MODELS WITH EXCEL

Excel provides an efficient way to analyze a multicriteria decision problem that can be described by a scoring model. We will use the job selection application from Section 17.3 to demonstrate this procedure.

A worksheet for the job selection scoring model is shown in Figure 17.7. The criteria weights are placed into cells B6 to B12. The ratings for each criterion and decision alternative are entered into cells C6 to E12.

The calculations used to compute the score for each decision alternative are shown in the bottom portion of the worksheet. The calculation for cell C18 is provided by the cell formula

$$=\$B6*C6$$

FIGURE 17.7   WORKSHEET FOR THE JOB SELECTION SCORING MODEL

EXCELfile
Scoring

	A	B	C	D	E	F
1	**Job Selection Scoring Model**					
2						
3				**Ratings**		
4			**Analyst**	**Accountant**	**Auditor**	
5	**Criteria**	**Weight**	**Chicago**	**Denver**	**Houston**	
6	Career Advancement	5	8	6	4	
7	Location	3	3	8	7	
8	Management	4	5	6	9	
9	Salary	3	6	7	5	
10	Prestige	2	7	5	4	
11	Job Security	4	4	7	6	
12	Enjoy the Work	5	8	6	5	
13						
14						
15	**Scoring Calculations**					
16			**Analyst**	**Accountant**	**Auditor**	
17	**Criteria**		**Chicago**	**Denver**	**Houston**	
18	Career Advancement		40	30	20	
19	Location		9	24	21	
20	Management		20	24	36	
21	Salary		18	21	15	
22	Prestige		14	10	8	
23	Job Security		16	28	24	
24	Enjoy the Work		40	30	25	
25						
26	**Score**		157	167	149	
27						

This cell formula can be copied from cell C18 to cells C18:E24 to provide the results shown in rows 18 to 24. The score for the financial analyst position in Chicago is found by placing the following formula in cell C26:

$$=SUM(C18:C24)$$

Copying cell C26 to cells D26:E26 provides the scores for the accountant in Denver and the auditor in Houston positions.

Appendix F   Self-Test Solutions and Answers to Even-Numbered Problems

Chapter 1

2. Define the problem; identify the alternatives; determine the criteria; evaluate the alternatives; choose an alternative

4. A quantitative approach should be considered because the problem is large, complex, important, new, and repetitive

6. Quicker to formulate, easier to solve, and/or more easily understood

8. a. Max $10x + 5y$
    s.t.
    $$5x + 2y \le 40$$
    $$x \ge 0, y \ge 0$$
   b. Controllable inputs: x and y
    Uncontrollable inputs: profit (10,5), labor-hours (5,2), and labor-hour availability (40)
   c. See Figure 1.8c
   d. $x = 0, y = 20$; Profit $= \$100$ (Solution by trial and error)
   e. Deterministic

10. a. Total units received $= x + y$
   b. Total cost $= 0.20x + 0.25y$
   c. $x + y = 5000$
   d. $x \le 4000$ Kansas City
    $y \le 3000$ Minneapolis
   e. Min $0.20x + 0.25y$
    s.t.
    $$x + \quad y = 5000$$
    $$x \quad\quad \le 4000$$
    $$y \le 3000$$
    $$x, y \ge 0$$

FIGURE 1.8c   SOLUTION

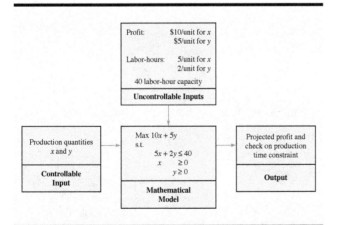

12. a. $TC = 1000 + 30x$
   b. $P = 40x - (1000 + 30x) = 10x - 1000$
   c. Break even when $P = 0$
    Thus $10x - 1000 = 0$
    $$10x = 1000$$
    $$x = 100$$

14. a. 4706
   b. Loss of $12,000
   c. $23
   d. $11,800

16. a. Max $6x + 4y$
   b. $50x + 30y \le 80,000$
    $50x \quad\quad \le 50,000$
    $30y \le 45,000$

Chapter 2

1. a. Record the number of persons waiting at the X-ray department at 9:00 A.M.
   b. The experimental outcomes (sample points) are the number of people waiting: 0, 1, 2, 3, and 4 (*Note:* Although it is theoretically possible for more than four people to be waiting, we use what has actually been observed to define the experimental outcomes.)
   c.

Number Waiting	Probability
0	.10
1	.25
2	.30
3	.20
4	.15
Total	1.00

   d. The relative frequency method

2. a. Choose a person at random, have them taste the four blends of coffee and state their preference
   b. Assign a probability of $\frac{1}{4}$ to each blend, using the classical method of equally likely outcomes
   c.

Blend	Probability
1	.20
2	.30
3	.35
4	.15
Total	1.00

The relative frequency method was used

4. a. Use the relative frequency approach:
   $P(\text{California}) = 1{,}434/2{,}374 = .60$

b. Number not from 4 states = $2{,}374 - 1{,}434 - 390 - 217 - 112 = 221$
   $P(\text{Not from 4 States}) = 221/2{,}374 = .09$

c. $P(\text{Not in Early Stages}) = 1 - .22 = .78$

d. Estimate of number of Massachusetts companies in early stage of development = $(.22)390 \approx 86$

e. If we assume the size of the awards did not differ by states, we can multiply the probability an award went to Colorado by the total venture funds disbursed to get an estimate

$$\text{Estimate of Colorado funds} = (112/2374)(\$32.4)$$
$$= \$1.53 \text{ billion}$$

(*Authors' Note:* The actual amount going to Colorado was $1.74 billion.)

6. a. $P(A) = P(150\text{--}199) + P(200 \text{ and over})$
$$= \frac{26}{100} + \frac{5}{100}$$
$$= 0.31$$

b. $P(B) = P(\text{less than } 50) + P(50\text{--}99) + P(100\text{--}149)$
$$= 0.13 + 0.22 + 0.34$$
$$= 0.69$$

7. a. $P(A) = 0.40, P(B) = 0.40, P(C) = 0.60$

b. $P(A \cup B) = P(E_1, E_2, E_3, E_4) = 0.80.$
   Yes, $P(A \cup B) = P(A) + P(B)$

c. $A^c = \{E_3, E_4, E_5\}; C^c = \{E_1, E_4\}; P(A^c) = 0.60;$
   $P(C^c) = 0.40$

d. $A \cup B^c = \{E_1, E_2, E_5\}; P(A \cup B^c) = 0.60$

e. $P(B \cup C) = P(E_2, E_3, E_4, E_5) = 0.80$

8. a. $0.5, 0.4, 0.2$

b. 0.70

c. 0.30

10. $P(\text{part-time job or dean's list}) = 0.50$

12. a. $P(A \mid B) = \dfrac{P(A \cap B)}{P(B)} = \dfrac{0.40}{0.60} = 0.6667$

b. $P(B \mid A) = \dfrac{P(A \cap B)}{P(A)} = \dfrac{0.40}{0.50} = 0.80$

c. No, because $P(A \mid B) \neq P(A)$

13. a.

Reason for Applying

	Quality	Cost/ Convenience	Other	Total
Full Time	0.218	0.204	0.039	0.461
Part Time	0.208	0.307	0.024	0.539
Total	0.426	0.511	0.063	1.000

b. A student will most likely cite cost or convenience as the first reason: probability = 0.511; school quality is the first reason cited by the second largest number of students: probability = 0.426

c. $P(\text{Quality} \mid \text{Full Time}) = 0.218/0.461 = 0.473$

d. $P(\text{Quality} \mid \text{Part Time}) = 0.208/0.539 = 0.386$

e. $P(B) = 0.426$ and $P(B \mid A) = 0.473$
   Since $P(B) \neq P(B \mid A)$, the events are dependent

14. a. 0.44

b. 0.15

c. 0.0225

d. 0.0025

e. 0.136

f. 0.106

16. a. 0.19

b. 0.71

c. 0.29

18. a. $0.25, 0.40, 0.10$

b. 0.25

c. Independent; program does not help

20. a. $P(B \cap A_1) = P(A_1)P(B \mid A_1) = (0.20)(0.50) = 0.10$
   $P(B \cap A_2) = P(A_2)P(B \mid A_2) = (0.50)(0.40) = 0.20$
   $P(B \cap A_3) = P(A_3)P(B \mid A_3) = (0.30)(0.30) = 0.09$

b. $P(A_2 \mid B) = \dfrac{0.20}{0.10 + 0.20 + 0.09} = 0.51$

c.

Events	$P(A_i)$	$P(B \mid A_i)$	$P(A_i \cap B)$	$P(A_i \mid B)$
A_1	0.20	0.50	0.10	0.26
A_2	0.50	0.40	0.20	0.51
A_3	0.30	0.30	0.09	0.23
	1.00		0.39	1.00

22. a. 0.40

b. 0.67

24. Let: S = small car
   S^c = other type of vehicle
   F = accident leads to fatality for vehicle occupant

We have $P(S) = .18$, so $P(S^c) = .82$; $P(F \mid S) = .128$ and $P(F \mid S^c) = .05$
Using the tabular form of Bayes' theorem provides:

Events	Prior Proba-bilities	Conditional Proba-bilities	Joint Proba-bilities	Posterior Proba-bilities
S	.18	.128	.023	.36
S^c	.82	.050	.041	.64
	1.00		.064	1.00

From the posterior probability column, we have $P(S \mid F) = .36$; so, if an accident leads to a fatality, the probability a small car was involved is .36

25. a. $P(\text{defective part}) = 0.0065$ (see below)

Events	$P(A_i)$	$P(D \mid A_i)$	$P(A_i \cap D)$	$P(A_i \mid D)$
Supplier A	0.60	0.0025	0.0015	0.23
Supplier B	0.30	0.0100	0.0030	0.46
Supplier C	0.10	0.0200	0.0020	0.31
	1.00		$P(D) = 0.0065$	1.00

b. Supplier B (prob. = 0.46) is the most likely source

26. a. $P(D_1 \mid S_1) = 0.2195$, $P(D_2 \mid S_1) = 0.7805$
b. $P(D_1 \mid S_2) = 0.50$, $P(D_2 \mid S_2) = 0.50$
c. $P(D_1 \mid S_3) = 0.8824$, $P(D_2 \mid S_3) = 0.1176$
d. 0.1582 and 0.8418

Chapter 3

1. a. Values: 0, 1, 2, . . . , 20
    discrete
b. Values: 0, 1, 2, . . .
    discrete
c. Values: 0, 1, 2, . . . , 50
    discrete
d. Values: $0 \leq x \leq 8$
    continuous
e. Values: $x \geq 0$
    continuous

2. a. 0.05; probability of a $200,000 profit
b. 0.70
c. 0.40

3. a.

x	$f(x)$
1	3/20 = 0.15
2	5/20 = 0.25
3	8/20 = 0.40
4	4/20 = 0.20
	Total 1.00

b.

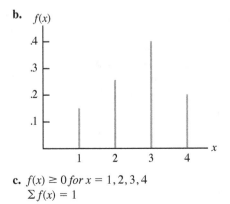

c. $f(x) \geq 0$ for $x = 1, 2, 3, 4$
    $\Sigma f(x) = 1$

4. a.

x	$f(x)$	$xf(x)$
3	0.25	0.75
6	0.50	3.00
9	0.25	2.25
Totals	1.00	6.00

$E(x) = \mu = 6.00$

b.

x	$x - \mu$	$(x - \mu)^2$	$f(x)$	$(x - \mu)^2 f(x)$
3	-3	9	0.25	2.25
6	0	0	0.50	0.00
9	3	9	0.25	2.25
				4.50

$\text{Var}(x) = \sigma^2 = 4.50$
c. $\sigma = \sqrt{4.50} = 2.12$

6. a.

x	$f(x)$
0	0.04
1	0.34
2	0.41
3	0.18
4+	0.04

b. $E(x) = 1.84$; $\text{Var}(x) = 0.79$
c.

y	$f(y)$
0	0.00
1	0.03
2	0.23
3	0.52
4+	0.22

d. $E(y) = 2.93$; $\text{Var}(y) = 0.59$
e. More bedrooms in owner-occupied houses

8. a. Medium 145; large 140; prefer medium
b. Medium 2725; large 12,400; prefer medium

9. a. $f(1) = \binom{2}{1}(0.4)^1(0.6)^1 = \dfrac{2!}{1!1!}(0.4)(0.6) = 0.48$

b. $f(0) = \binom{2}{0}(0.4)^0(0.6)^2 = \dfrac{2!}{0!2!}(1)(0.36) = 0.36$

c. $f(2) = \binom{2}{2}(0.4)^2(0.6)^0 = \dfrac{2!}{2!0!}(0.16)(1) = 0.16$

d. $P(x \geq 1) = f(1) + f(2) = 0.48 + 0.16 = 0.64$
e. $E(x) = np = 2(0.4) = 0.8$
    $\text{Var}(x) = np(1 - p) = 2(0.4)(0.6) = 0.48$
    $\sigma = \sqrt{0.48} = 0.6928$

10. a. $f(0) = 0.3487$
b. $f(2) = 0.1937$
c. 0.9298

d. 0.6513

e. 1

f. $\sigma^2 = 0.9000, \sigma = 0.9487$

12. a. Probability of a defective part being produced must be 0.03 for each trial; trials must be independent

b. Two outcomes result in exactly one defect

c. $P(\text{no defects}) = (0.97)(0.97) = 0.9409$
$P(1 \text{ defect}) = 2(0.03)(0.97) = 0.0582$
$P(2 \text{ defects}) = (0.03)(0.03) = 0.0009$

14. a. $f(x) = \dfrac{2^x e^{-2}}{x!}$

b. $\mu = 6$ for 3 time periods

c. $f(x) = \dfrac{6^x e^{-6}}{x!}$

d. $f(2) = \dfrac{2^2 e^{-2}}{2!} = \dfrac{4(0.1353)}{2} = 0.2706$

e. $f(6) = \dfrac{6^6 e^{-6}}{6!} = 0.1606$

f. $f(5) = \dfrac{4^5 e^{-4}}{5!} = 0.1563$

16. a. 0.0009

b. 0.9927

c. 0.0302

d. 0.8271

18. a.

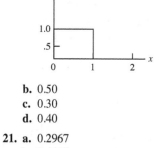

b. $P(x = 1.25) = 0$; the probability of any single point is zero because the area under the curve above any single point is zero

c. $P(1.0 \le x \le 1.25) = 2(0.25) = 0.50$

d. $P(1.2 < x < 1.5) = 2(0.30) = 0.60$

20. a.

b. 0.50

c. 0.30

d. 0.40

21. a. 0.2967

b. 0.4418

c. $0.5000 - 0.1700 = 0.3300$

d. $0.0910 + 0.5000 = 0.5910$

e. $0.3849 + 0.5000 = 0.8849$

f. $0.5000 - 0.2612 = 0.2388$

22. a. 1.96

b. 0.61

c. 1.12

d. 0.44

23. a. Look in the table for an area of $0.5000 - 0.2119 = 0.2881$; the value we are seeking is below the mean, so the z value must be negative; thus, for an area of $0.2881, z = -0.80$

b. Look in the table for an area of $0.9030/2 = 0.4515$; $z = 1.66$

c. Look in the table for an area of $0.2052/2 = 0.1026$; $z = 0.26$

d. Look in the table for an area of $0.9948 - 0.5000 = 0.4948; z = 2.56$

e. Look in the table for an area of $0.6915 - 0.5000 = 0.1915$; the value we are seeking is below the mean, so the z value must be negative; thus, $z = -0.50$

24. a. 0.3830

b. 0.1056

c. 0.0062

d. 0.1603

26. a. 0.7745

b. 36.32

c. 19%

28. $\mu = 19.23$

29. a. $P(x \le x_0) = 1 - e^{-x_0/3}$

b. $P(x \le 2) = 1 - e^{-2/3} = 1 - 0.5134 = 0.4866$

c. $P(x \ge 3) = 1 - P(x \le 3) = 1 - (1 - e^{-3/3}) = e^{-1} = 0.3679$

d. $P(x \le 5) = 1 - e^{-5/3} = 1 - 0.1889 = 0.8111$

e. $P(2 \le x \le 5) = P(x \le 5) - P(x \le 2) = 0.8111 - 0.4866 = 0.3245$

30. a. 0.3935

b. 0.2231

b. 0.3834

31. a.

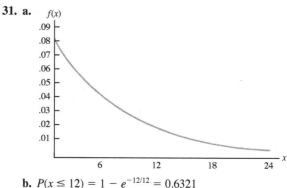

b. $P(x \le 12) = 1 - e^{-12/12} = 0.6321$

c. $P(x \le 6) = 1 - e^{-6/12} = 0.3935$

d. $P(x \ge 30) = 1 - P(x < 30) = 1 - (1 - e^{-30/12}) = 0.0821$

32. a. 50 hours

b. 0.3935

c. 0.1353

34. a. 0.5130

b. 0.1655

c. 0.3679

Chapter 4

1. a.

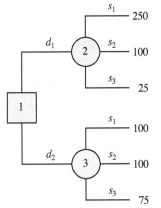

b.

Decision	Maximum Profit	Minimum Profit
d_1	250	25
d_2	100	75

Optimistic approach: Select d_1
Conservative approach: Select d_2

Regret or opportunity loss table:

Decision	s_1	s_2	s_3
d_1	0	0	50
d_2	150	0	0

Maximum regret: 50 for d_1 and 150 for d_2; select d_1

2. a. Optimistic: d_1
Conservative: d_3
Minimax regret: d_3
c. Optimistic: d_1
Conservative: d_2 or d_3
Minimax regret: d_2

3. a. Decision: choose the best plant size from the two alternatives: a small plant and a large plant
Chance event: market demand for the new product line with three possible outcomes (states of nature): low, medium, and high
b. Influence Diagram:

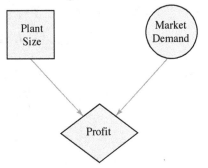

c.

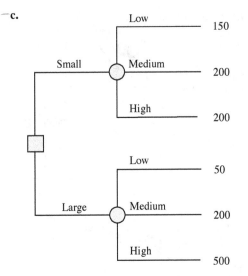

d.

Decision	Maximum Profit	Minimum Profit	Maximum Regret
Small	200	150	300
Large	500	50	100

Optimistic Approach: Large Plant
Conservative Approach: Small Plant
Minimax Regret: Large Plant

4. a. Decision: Which lease option to choose
Chance event: Miles driven

b.

	Annual Miles Driven		
	12,000	15,000	18,000
Forno	10,764	12,114	13,464
Midtown	11,160	11,160	12,960
Hopkins	11,700	11,700	11,700

c. Optimistic: Forno Saab
Conservative: Hopkins Automotive
Minimax: Hopkins Automotive
d. Midtown Motors
e. Most likely: $11,160; Probability = 0.9
f. Midtown Motors or Hopkins Automotive

5. a. $EV(d_1) = 0.65(250) + 0.15(100) + 0.20(25) = 182.5$
$EV(d_2) = 0.65(100) + 0.15(100) + 0.20(75) = 95$
The optimal decision is d_1

6. a. Pharmaceuticals; 3.4%
b. Financial; 4.6%

7. a. $EV(\text{own staff}) = 0.2(650) + 0.5(650) + 0.3(600)$
$= 635$

EV(outside vendor) = 0.2(900) + 0.5(600)
$$+ 0.3(300) = 570$$
EV(combination) = 0.2(800) + 0.5(650) + 0.3(500)
$$= 635$$

Optimal decision: hire an outside vendor with an expected cost of $570,000

b.

	Cost	Probability
Own staff	300	0.3
Outside vendor	600	0.5
Combination	900	0.2
		1.0

8. a. $EV(d_1) = p(10) + (1 - p)(1) = 9p + 1$
$EV(d_2) = p(4) + (1 - p)(3) = 1p + 3$

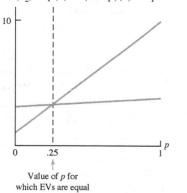

Value of p for
which EVs are equal

$9p + 1 = 1p + 3$ and hence $p = 0.25$
d_2 is optimal for $p \leq 0.25$, d_1 is optimal for $p \geq 0.25$
b. d_2
c. As long as the payoff for $s_1 \geq 2$, then d_2 is optimal

10. b. Space Pirates
EV = $724,000
$84,000 better than Battle Pacific
c.
$200	0.18
$400	0.32
$800	0.30
$1600	0.20
d. $P(\text{Competition}) > 0.7273$

12. a. Decision: Whether to lengthen the runway
Chance Event: The location decisions of Air Express and DRI
Consequence: Annual revenue
b. $255,000
c. $270,000
d. No
e. Lengthen the runway

14. a. If s_1, then d_1; if s_2, then d_1 or d_2; if s_3, then d_2
b. EVwPI = 0.65(250) + 0.15(100) + 0.20(75) = 192.5
c. From the solution to Problem 5, we know that EV(d_1) = 182.5 and EV(d_2) = 95; thus, recommended decision is d_1; hence, EVwoPI = 182.5
d. EVPI = EVwPI − EVwoPI = 192.5 − 182.5 = 10

16. a.

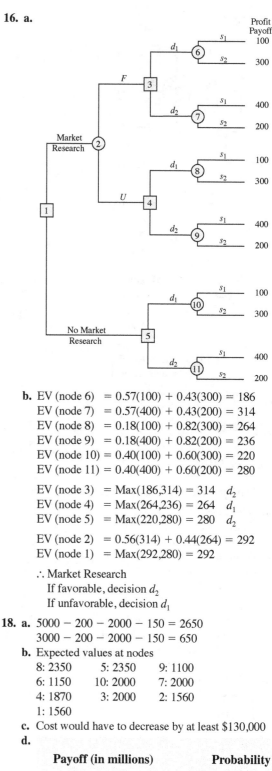

b. EV (node 6) = 0.57(100) + 0.43(300) = 186
EV (node 7) = 0.57(400) + 0.43(200) = 314
EV (node 8) = 0.18(100) + 0.82(300) = 264
EV (node 9) = 0.18(400) + 0.82(200) = 236
EV (node 10) = 0.40(100) + 0.60(300) = 220
EV (node 11) = 0.40(400) + 0.60(200) = 280

EV (node 3) = Max(186,314) = 314 d_2
EV (node 4) = Max(264,236) = 264 d_1
EV (node 5) = Max(220,280) = 280 d_2

EV (node 2) = 0.56(314) + 0.44(264) = 292
EV (node 1) = Max(292,280) = 292

∴ Market Research
  If favorable, decision d_2
  If unfavorable, decision d_1

18. a. 5000 − 200 − 2000 − 150 = 2650
3000 − 200 − 2000 − 150 = 650
b. Expected values at nodes
8: 2350   5: 2350   9: 1100
6: 1150   10: 2000   7: 2000
4: 1870   3: 2000   2: 1560
1: 1560
c. Cost would have to decrease by at least $130,000
d.

Payoff (in millions)	Probability
−$200	0.20
800	0.32
2800	0.48
	1.00

20. b. If Do Not Review, Accept
If Review and F, Accept
If Review and U, Accept
Always Accept
c. Do not review; EVSI = $0
d. $87,500; better method of predicting success

22. a. Order 2 lots; $60,000
b. If E, order 2 lots
If V, order 1 lot
EV = $60,500
c. EVPI = $14,000
EVSI = $500
Efficiency = 3.6%
Yes, use consultant

23.

State of Nature	$P(s_j)$	$P(I/s_j)$	$P(I \cap s_j)$	$P(s_j/I)$
s_1	0.2	0.10	0.020	0.1905
s_2	0.5	0.05	0.025	0.2381
s_3	0.3	0.20	0.060	0.5714
	1.0		$P(I) = 0.105$	1.0000

24. a. 0.695, 0.215, 0.090
0.98, 0.02
0.79, 0.21
0.00, 1.00
c. If C, Expressway
If O, Expressway
If R, Queen City
26.6 minutes

Chapter 5

1. a. $EV(d_1) = 0.40(100) + 0.30(25) + 0.30(0) = 47.5$
$EV(d_2) = 0.40(75) + 0.30(50) + 0.30(25) = 52.5 \ \}d_2$
$EV(d_3) = 0.40(50) + 0.30(50) + 0.30(50) = 50.0$
b. Using utilities

Decision Maker A	Decision Maker B
$EU(d_1) = 4.9$	$EU(d_1) = 4.45$ Best
$EU(d_2) = 5.9$	$EU(d_2) = 3.75$
$EU(d_3) = 6.0$ Best	$EU(d_3) = 3.00$

c. Difference in attitude toward risk; decision maker A tends to avoid risk, whereas decision maker B tends to take a risk for the opportunity of a large payoff

2. a. d_2; $EV(d_2) = $5,000$
b. p = probability of a $0 cost
$1 - p$ = probability of a $200,000 cost
c. d_1; $EV(d_1) = 9.9$
d. Expected utility approach; it avoids risk of large loss

4. a. Route B; EV = 58.5
b. p = probability of a 45-minute travel time
$1 - p$ = probability of a 90-minute travel time
c. Route A; EV = 7.6; risk-avoider

5. a.

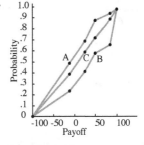

b. A—risk avoider
B—risk taker
C—risk neutral
c. Risk-avoider A, at $20 payoff $p = 0.70$
∴ EV(Lottery) = 0.70(100) + 0.30(−100) = $40
∴ Will pay 40 − 20 = $20
Risk-taker B, at $20 payoff $p = 0.45$
∴ EV(Lottery) = 0.45(100) + 0.55(−100) = −$10
∴ Will pay 20 − (−10) = $30

6. A: d_1; B: d_2; C: d_2

8. a.

	Win	Lose
Bet	350	−10
Do not bet	0	0

b. d_2
c. Risk takers
d. Between 0 and 0.26

10. a. Western; EV = 26%
b. p = probability of a 40% show
$1 - p$ = probability of a 15% show
c. Musical; risk taker

11.

		Player B			
		b_1	b_2	b_3	Minimum
Player A	a_1	8	5	7	⑤
	a_2	2	4	10	2
	Maximum	8	⑤	10	

The maximum of the row minimums is 5 and the minimum of the column maximums is 5. The game has a pure strategy. Player A should take strategy a_1 and Player B should take strategy b_2. The value of the game is 5.

12. Pure Strategy
A: a_2 news program
B: b_3 home improvement
Station A gains 6000

14. a. Strategy a_3 dominated by a_2
Strategy b_1 dominated by b_2

		Player B	
		b_2	b_3
Player A	a_1	-1	2
	a_2	4	-3

b. Let p = probability of a_1
and $(1-p)$ = probability of a_2
If b_1, EV $= -1p + 4(1-p)$
If b_2, EV $= 2p - 3(1-p)$

$$-1p + 4(1-p) = 2p - 3(1-p)$$
$$-1p + 4 - 4p = 2p - 3 + 3p$$
$$10p = 7$$
$$p = 0.70$$

$P(a_1) = p = 0.70$
$P(a_2) = 1 - 0.70 = 0.30$

Let q = probability of b_2
and $(1-q)$ = probability of b_3
If a_1, EV $= -1q + 2(1-q)$
If a_2, EV $= 4q - 3(1-q)$

$$-1q + 2(1-q) = 4q - 3(1-q)$$
$$-1q + 2 - 2q = 4q - 3 + 3q$$
$$10q = 5$$
$$q = 0.50$$

$P(b_2) = q = 0.50$
$P(b_3) = 1 - 0.50 = 0.50$

c. $-1p + 4(1-p) = -(0.70) + 4(0.30)$
$$= +0.50$$

16. A: $P(a_3) = 0.80, P(a_4) = 0.20$
B: $P(b_1) = 0.40, P(b_2) = 0.60$
Value = 2.8

Chapter 6

1. a.

Month	Time Series Value	3-Month Moving Average Forecast	(Error)^2	4-Month Moving Average Forecast	(Error)^2
1	9.5				
2	9.3				
3	9.4				
4	9.6	9.40	0.04		
5	9.8	9.43	0.14	9.45	0.12
6	9.7	9.60	0.01	9.53	0.03
7	9.8	9.70	0.01	9.63	0.03
8	10.5	9.77	0.53	9.73	0.59
9	9.9	10.00	0.01	9.95	0.00
10	9.7	10.07	0.14	9.98	0.08
11	9.6	10.03	0.18	9.97	0.14
12	9.6	9.73	0.02	9.92	0.10
		Totals	1.08		1.09

MSE(3-month) = 1.08/9 = 0.12
MSE(4-month) = 1.09/8 = 0.14
Use a three-month moving average.
b. Forecast = $(9.7 + 9.6 + 9.6)/3 = 9.63$

2. a.

Week	Time Series Value	4-Week Moving Average Forecast	(Error)^2	5-Week Moving Average Forecast	(Error)^2
1	17				
2	21				
3	19				
4	23				
5	18	20.00	4.00		
6	16	20.25	18.06	19.60	12.96
7	20	19.00	1.00	19.40	0.36
8	18	19.25	1.56	19.20	1.44
9	22	18.00	16.00	19.00	9.00
10	20	19.00	1.00	18.80	1.44
11	15	20.00	25.00	19.20	17.64
12	22	18.75	10.56	19.00	9.00
		Totals	77.18		51.84

b. MSE(4-week) = 77.18/8 = 9.65
MSE(5-week) = 51.84/7 = 7.41
c. For the limited data provided, the five-week moving average provides the smallest MSE

4.

Week	Time Series Value	Forecast	Error	(Error)^2
1	17			
2	21	17.00	4.00	16.00
3	19	17.40	1.60	2.56
4	23	17.56	5.44	29.59
5	18	18.10	-0.10	0.01
6	16	18.09	-2.09	4.37
7	20	17.88	2.12	4.49
8	18	18.10	-0.10	0.01
9	22	18.09	3.91	15.29
10	20	18.48	1.52	2.31
11	15	18.63	-3.63	13.18
12	22	18.27	3.73	13.91
			Total	101.72

MSE = 101.72/11 = 9.25
$\alpha = 0.2$ provided a lower MSE
therefore $\alpha = 0.2$ is better than $\alpha = 0.1$

5. a.

Month	Y_t	3-Month Moving Averages Forecast	(Error)^2	$\alpha = 2$ Forecast	(Error)^2
1	80				
2	82			80.00	4.00

(continued)

Month	Y_t	3-Month Moving Averages Forecast	$(Error)^2$	$\alpha = 2$ Forecast	$(Error)^2$
3	84			80.40	12.96
4	83	82.00	1.00	81.12	3.53
5	83	83.00	0.00	81.50	2.25
6	84	83.33	0.45	81.80	4.84
7	85	83.33	2.79	82.24	7.62
8	84	84.00	0.00	82.79	1.46
9	82	84.33	5.43	83.03	1.06
10	83	83.67	0.45	82.83	0.03
11	84	83.00	1.00	82.86	1.30
12	83	83.00	0.00	83.09	0.01
		Totals	11.12		39.06

MSE(3-month) = 11.12/9 = 1.24
MSE($\alpha = 0.2$) = 39.06/11 = 3.55
Use a three-month moving average

b. (83 + 84 + 83)/3 = 83.3

6. b. The more recent data receive the greater weight or importance in determining the forecast

8. a. 15.71
   b. 15.74
   c. 15.51
   d. Moving averages; it has the smallest MSE (0.60)

10. a. $\alpha = 0.1$
   b. 29.99

12. 3117.01

14. $\sum t = 21; \sum t^2 = 91; \sum Y_t = 117.1;$

$\sum tY_t = 403.7; n = 6$

$$b_1 = \frac{\sum tY_t - (\sum t \sum Y_t)/n}{\sum t^2 - (\sum t)^2/n}$$

$$= \frac{403.7 - (21)(117.1)/6}{91 - (21)^2/6}$$

$$= -0.3514$$

$b_0 = \bar{Y} - b_1\bar{t} = 19.5167 - (-.3514)(3.5) = 20.7466$

$T_t = 20.7466 - 0.3514t$

Conclusion: Enrollment appears to be decreasing by an average of approximately 351 students per year

16. a. Linear trend appears to be reasonable
   b. $T_t = 19.993 + 1.774t$
   Average cost increase of $1.77 per unit per year

18. a. The graph shows a linear trend
   b. $T_t = 60.553 - 1.141t$; 1.14%
   c. 48.0%

20. a. A linear trend appears to exist
   b. $T_t = -5 + 15t$
   Average increase in sales is 15 units per year

22. a. A linear trend appears to be appropriate
   b. $T_t = 6.4564 + 0.5345t$
   c. 5.345 million
   d. 2001–2002 season: $T_{13} = 6.4564 + 0.5345(12) = 12.87$ million

24. a. Forecast for July is 236.97; forecast for August is 236.97
   b. Forecast for July is 278.88; forecast for August is 297.33
   c. Not fair; it does not account for upward trend in sales

25. a. Four-quarter moving averages beginning with $(1690 + 940 + 2625 + 2500)/4 = 1938.75$
   Other moving averages are

1966.25	2002.50
1956.25	2052.50
2025.00	2060.00
1990.00	2123.75

   b.

Quarter	Seasonal-Irregular Component Values		Seasonal Index	Adjusted Seasonal Index
1	0.904	0.900	0.9020	0.900
2	0.448	0.526	0.4970	0.486
3	1.344	1.453	1.3985	1.396
4	1.275	1.164	1.2195	1.217
		Total	4.0070	

   Note: Adjustment for seasonal index = 4.000/4.007 = 0.9983

   c. The largest seasonal effect is in the third quarter, which corresponds to the back-to-school demand during July, August, and September of each year

26. 0.707, 0.777, 0.827, 0.966, 1.016, 1.305, 1.494, 1.225, 0.976, 0.986, 0.936, 0.787

28. a. Selected centered moving averages for $t = 5, 10, 15,$ and 20 are 11.125, 18.125, 22.875, and 27.000
   b. 0.899, 1.362, 1.118, 0.621
   c. Quarter 2, prior to summer boating season

30. a. $T_t = 6.329 + 1.055t$
   b. 36.92, 37.98, 39.03, 40.09
   c. 33.23, 51.65, 43.71, 24.86

32. a. Yes, there is a seasonal effect; seasonal indexes are 1.696, 1.458, 0.711, 0.326, 0.448, 1.362
   b. Forecast for 12–4 is 166,761.13; forecast for 4–8 is 146,052.99

33. a.

Restaurant

(i)	x_i	y_i	$x_i y_i$	x_i^2
1	1	19	19	1
2	4	44	176	16
3	6	40	240	36
4	10	52	520	100
5	14	53	742	196
Totals	35	208	1697	349

$$\bar{x} = \frac{35}{5} = 7$$

$$\bar{y} = \frac{208}{5} = 41.6$$

$$b_1 = \frac{\sum x_i y_i - (\sum x_i \sum y_i)/n}{\sum x_i^2 - (\sum x_i)^2/n}$$

$$= \frac{1697 - (35)(208)/5}{349 - (35)^2/5}$$

$$= \frac{241}{104} = 2.317$$

$$b_0 = \bar{y} - b_1 \bar{x} = 41.6 - 2.317(7) = 25.381$$

$$\hat{y} = 25.381 + 2.317x$$

b. $\hat{y} = 25.381 + 2.317(8) = 43.917$, or $43,917

34. a. $\hat{y} = 37.666 - 3.222x$

b. $3444

Chapter 7

1. Parts (a), (b), and (e) are acceptable linear programming relationships

Part (c) is not acceptable because of $-2x_2^2$

Part (d) is not acceptable because of $3\sqrt{x_1}$

Part (f) is not acceptable because of $1x_1 x_2$

Parts (c), (d), and (f) could not be found in a linear programming model because they contain nonlinear terms

2. a.

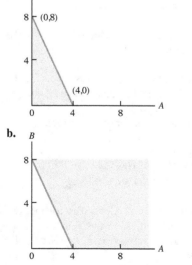

c.

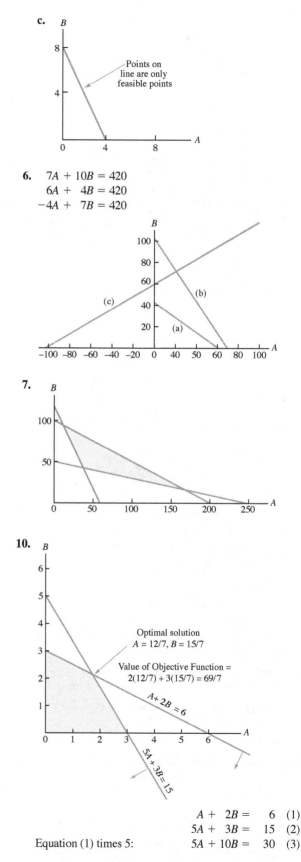

6.
$$7A + 10B = 420$$
$$6A + 4B = 420$$
$$-4A + 7B = 420$$

7.

10.

$$A + 2B = 6 \quad (1)$$
$$5A + 3B = 15 \quad (2)$$
Equation (1) times 5: $\quad 5A + 10B = 30 \quad (3)$

Equation (2) minus equation (3): $-7B = -15$
$$B = 15/7$$
From equation (1): $A = 6 - 2(15/7)$
$$= 6 - 30/7 = 12/7$$

12. a. $A = 3, B = 1.5$; Value of optimal solution $= 13.5$
  b. $A = 0, B = 3$; Value of optimal solution $= 18$
  c. four: $(0, 0), (4, 0), (3, 1.5)$, and (0.3)

13. a.

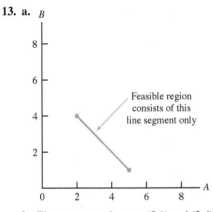

  b. The extreme points are $(5,1)$ and $(2,4)$
  c.

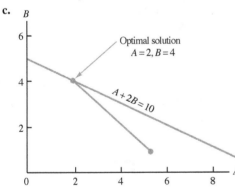

14. a. 540 standard bags, 252 deluxe bags
  b. \$7668
  c. $630, 480, 708, 117$
  d. $0, 120, 0, 18$

16. a. $3S + 9D$
  b. $(0,540)$
  c. $90, 150, 348, 0$

17. Max $5A + 2B + 0s_1 + 0s_2 + 0s_3$
  s.t.
$$1A - 2B + 1s_1 \qquad\qquad = 420$$
$$2A + 3B - \quad + 1s_2 \qquad = 610$$
$$6A - 1B + \qquad\quad + 1s_3 = 125$$
$$A, B, s_1, s_2, s_3 \geq 0$$

18. b. $A = 18/7, B = 15/7$
  c. $0, 0, 4/7$

20. b. $A = 3.43, B = 3.43$
  c. $2.86, 0, 1.43, 0$

22. b.

Extreme Point	Coordinates	Profit (\$)
1	$(0, 0)$	0
2	$(1700, 0)$	8500
3	$(1400, 600)$	9400
4	$(800, 1200)$	8800
5	$(0, 1680)$	6720

Extreme point 3 generates the highest profit
  c. $A = 1400, C = 600$
  d. Cutting and dyeing constraint and the packaging constraint
  e. $A = 800, C = 1200$; profit $= \$9200$

24. a. Let $R =$ number of units of regular model
$C =$ number of units of catcher's model
  Max $5R + 8C$
$$1R + \tfrac{3}{2}C \leq 900 \quad \text{Cutting and sewing}$$
$$\tfrac{1}{2}R + \tfrac{1}{3}C \leq 300 \quad \text{Finishing}$$
$$\tfrac{1}{8}R + \tfrac{1}{4}C \leq 100 \quad \text{Packaging and shipping}$$
$$R, C \geq 0$$
  b.

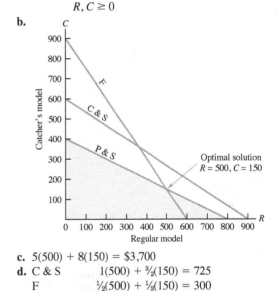

  c. $5(500) + 8(150) = \$3,700$
  d. C & S $1(500) + \tfrac{3}{2}(150) = 725$
    F $\tfrac{1}{2}(500) + \tfrac{1}{3}(150) = 300$
    P & S $\tfrac{1}{8}(500) + \tfrac{1}{4}(150) = 100$
  e.

Department	Capacity	Usage	Slack
Cutting and sewing	900	725	175 hours
Finishing	300	300	0 hours
Packaging and shipping	100	100	0 hours

26. a. Max $50N + 80R$
  s.t.
$$N + \quad R = 1000$$
$$N \qquad\qquad \geq 250$$
$$R \geq 250$$
$$N - 2R \geq \quad 0$$
$$N, R \geq 0$$
  b. $N = 666.67, R = 333.33$; Audience exposure $= 60,000$

28. a. Max $1W + 1.25M$
    s.t.

$$5W + \quad 7M \le 4480$$
$$3W + \quad 1M \le 2080$$
$$2W + \quad 2M \le 1600$$
$$W, M \ge 0$$

b. $W = 560, M = 240$; Profit $= 860$

30. a. Max $15E + 18C$
    s.t.

$$40E + 25C \le 50,000$$
$$40E \qquad\quad \ge 15,000$$
$$25C \ge 10,000$$
$$25C \le 25,000$$
$$E, C \ge 0$$

c. $(375, 400); (1000, 400); (625, 1000); (375, 1000)$
d. $E = 625, C = 1000$
    Total return $= \$27,375$

31.

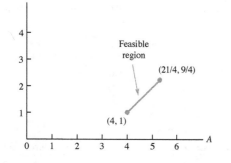

Optimal solution
$A = 3, B = 1$

$3A + 4B = 13$

Objective function value $= 13$

32.

Extreme Points	Objective Function Value	Surplus Demand	Surplus Total Production	Slack Processing Time
(250, 100)	800	125	—	—
(125, 225)	925	—	—	125
(125, 350)	1300	—	125	—

34. a.

b. There are two extreme points
    $(A = 4, B = 1)$ and $(A = 21/4, B = 9/4)$
c. The optimal solution (see part (a)) is $A = 4, B = 1$

35. a. Min $6A + 4B + 0s_1 + 0s_2 + 0s_3$
    s.t.

$$2A + 1B - \ s_1 \qquad\qquad = 12$$
$$1A + 1B \qquad - s_2 \qquad = 10$$
$$1B \qquad\qquad + \ s_3 = 4$$
$$A, B, s_1, s_2, s_3 \ge 0$$

b. The optimal solution is $A = 6, B = 4$
c. $s_1 = 4, s_2 = 0, s_3 = 0$

36. a. Min $10,000T + 8,000P$
    s.t.

$$T \qquad\qquad \ge \ 8$$
$$P \ge 10$$
$$T + \qquad P \ge 25$$
$$3T + \quad 2P \le 84$$

c. $(15, 10); (21.33, 10); (8, 30); (8, 17)$
d. $T = 8, P = 17$
    Total cost $= \$216,000$

38. a. Min $7.50S + 9.00P$
    s.t.

$$0.10S + 0.30P \ge \ 6$$
$$0.06S + 0.12P \le \ 3$$
$$S + \qquad P = 30$$
$$S, P \ge 0$$

c. Optional solution is $S = 15, P = 15$
d. No
e. Yes

40. $P_1 = 30, P_2 = 25$, Cost $= \$55$

42.

43.

44. a. $A = {}^{30}\!/_{16}, B = {}^{30}\!/_{16}$; Value of optimal solution $= {}^{60}\!/_{16}$
   b. $A = 0, B = 3$; Value of optimal solution $= 6$

46. a. $180, 20$
   b. Alternative optimal solutions
   c. $120, 80$

48. No feasible solution

50. $M = 65.45, R = 261.82$; Profit $= \$45,818$

52. $S = 384, O = 80$

54. a. Max $\quad 160M_1 + 345M_2$
   s.t.
$$
\begin{aligned}
M_1 &\;\;\;\;\;\;\;\;\;\;\; \le \;\; 15 \\
&\;\;\; M_2 \le \;\; 10 \\
M_1 &\;\;\;\;\;\;\;\;\;\;\; \ge \;\;\; 5 \\
&\;\;\; M_2 \ge \;\;\; 5 \\
40M_1 &+ 50M_2 \le 1000 \\
M_1, M_2 &\ge 0
\end{aligned}
$$
   b. $M_1 = 12.5, M_2 = 10$

Chapter 8

1. a.

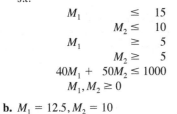
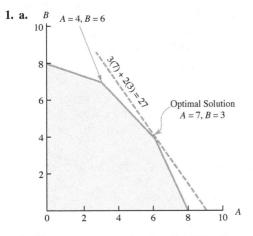

   b. The same extreme point, $A = 7$ and $B = 3$, remains optimal; Value of the objective function becomes $5(7) + 2(3) = 41$
   c. A new extreme point, $A = 4$ and $B = 6$, becomes optimal; Value of the objective function becomes $3(4) + 4(6) = 36$
   d. The objective coefficient range for variable A is 2 to 6; the optimal solution, $A = 7$ and $B = 3$, does not change The objective coefficient range for variable B is 1 to 3; resolve the problem to find the new optimal solution

2. a. The feasible region becomes larger with the new optimal solution of $A = 6.5$ and $B = 4.5$
   b. Value of the optimal solution to the revised problem is $3(6.5) + 2(4.5) = 28.5$; the one-unit increase in the right-hand side of constraint 1 improves the value of the optimal solution by $28.5 - 27 = 1.5$, therefore, the dual price for constraint 1 is 1.5

   c. The right-hand-side range for constraint 1 is 8 to 11.2; as long as the right-hand side stays within this range, the dual price of 1.5 is applicable
   d. The improvement in the value of the optimal solution will be 0.5 for every unit increase in the right-hand side of constraint 2 as long as the right-hand side is between 18 and 30

4. a. $X = 2.5, Y = 2.5$
   b. -2
   c. 5 to 11
   d. -3 between 9 and 18

5. a. Regular glove $= 500$; Catcher's mitt $= 150$;
   Value $= 3700$
   b. The finishing, packaging, and shipping constraints are binding; there is no slack
   c. Cutting and sewing $= 0$
   Finishing $= 3$
   Packaging and shipping $= 28$
   Additional finishing time is worth \$3 per unit, and additional packaging and shipping time is worth \$28 per unit
   d. In the packaging and shipping department, each additional hour is worth \$28

6. a. 4 to 12
   3.33 to 10
   b. As long as the profit contribution for the regular glove is between \$4.00 and \$12.00, the current solution is optimal; as long as the profit contribution for the catcher's mitt stays between \$3.33 and \$10.00, the current solution is optimal; the optimal solution is not sensitive to small changes in the profit contributions for the gloves
   c. The dual prices for the resources are applicable over the following ranges:

Constraint	Right-Hand-Side Range
Cutting and sewing	725 to No Upper Limit
Finishing	133.33 to 400
Packaging and shipping	75 to 135

   d. Amount of increase $= (28)(20) = \$560$

8. a. More than \$7.00
   b. More than \$3.50
   c. None

10. a. $S = 4000, M = 10,000$, Total risk $= 62,000$
   b.

Variable	Objective Coefficient Range
S	3.75 to No Upper Limit
M	No Lower Limit to 6.4

   c. $5(4000) + 4(10,000) = \$60,000$
   d. $60,000 / 1,200,000 = 0.05$ or 5%
   e. 0.057 risk units
   f. $0.057(100) = 5.7\%$

12. a. $E = 80, S = 120, D = 0$
  Profit = \$16,440
  b. Fan motors and cooling coils
  c. Labor hours; 320 hours available
  d. Objective function coefficient range of optimality
  No Lower Limit to 159
  Because \$150 is in this range, the optimal solution would not change

13. a. Range of optimality
  E 47.5 to 75
  S 87 to 126
  D No Lower Limit to 159

b.

Model	Profit	Change	Allowable Increase/Decrease	%
E	\$ 63	Increase \$6(100)	$75 - $63 = $12	$\%_{12}(100) = 50$
S	\$ 95	Decrease \$2	$95 - $87 = $8	$\frac{2}{8}(100) = 25$
D	\$135	Increase \$4	$159 - $135 = $24	$\frac{4}{24}(100) = 17$
				$\overline{92}$

Because changes are 92% of allowable changes, the optimal solution of $E = 80, S = 120, D = 0$ will not change
  The change in total profit will be
  E 80 units @ +\$6 = \$480
  S 120 units @ −\$2 = $\underline{-240}$
                      \$240
  ∴ Profit = \$16,440 + \$240 = \$16,680

  c. Range of feasibility
  Constraint 1   160 to 280
  Constraint 2   200 to 400
  Constraint 3   2080 to No Upper Limit

  d. Yes, Fan motors = 200 + 100 = 300 is outside the range of feasibility; the dual price will change

14. a. Manufacture 100 cases of A and 60 cases of B, and purchase 90 cases of B; Total cost = \$2170
  b. Demand for A, demand for B, assembly time
  c. $-12.25, -9.0, 0, .375$
  d. Assembly time constraint

16. a. 100 suits, 150 sport coats
  Profit = \$40,900
  40 hours of cutting overtime
  b. Optimal solution will not change
  c. Consider ordering additional material
  \$34.50 is the maximum price
  d. Profit will improve by \$875

18. a. The linear programming model is as follows:
  Min $30AN + 50AO + 25BN + 40BO$
  s.t.

$$
\begin{aligned}
AN + AO &\geq 50{,}000 \\
BN + BO &\geq 70{,}000 \\
AN + BN &\leq 80{,}000 \\
AO + BO &\leq 60{,}000 \\
AN, AO, BN, BO &\geq 0
\end{aligned}
$$

b. Optimal solution

	New Line	Old Line
Model A	50,000	0
Model B	30,000	40,000

Total cost: \$3,850,000

c. The first three constraints are binding
d. Because the dual price is positive, increasing the right-hand side of constraint 3 will *improve* the solution; thus, an increase in capacity for the new production line is desirable
e. Because constraint 4 is not a binding constraint, any increase in the production line capacity of the old production line will have no effect on the optimal solution; thus, increasing the capacity of the old production line results in no benefit
f. The reduced cost for model A made on the old production line is 5; thus, the cost would have to decrease by at least \$5 before any units of model A would be produced on the old production line
g. The right-hand-side range for constraint 2 shows a lower limit of 30,000; thus, if the minimum production requirement is reduced 10,000 units to 60,000, the dual price of −40 is applicable; thus, total cost would decrease by 10,000(40) = \$400,000

20. a. Max $0.07H + 0.12P + 0.09A$
  s.t.

$$
\begin{aligned}
H + P + A &= 1{,}000{,}000 \\
0.6H - 0.4P - 0.4A &\geq 0 \\
P - 0.6A &\leq 0 \\
H, P, A &\geq 0
\end{aligned}
$$

b. $H = $400{,}000, P = $225{,}000, A = $375{,}000$
  Total annual return = \$88,750
  Annual percentage return = 8.875%
c. No change
d. Increase of \$890
e. Increase of \$312.50 or 0.031%

22. a. Min $30L + 25D + 18S$
  s.t.

$$
\begin{aligned}
L + D + S &= 100 \\
0.6L - 0.4D &\geq 0 \\
-0.15L - 0.15D + 0.85S &\geq 0 \\
-0.25L - 0.25D + S &\leq 0 \\
L &\leq 50 \\
L, D, S &\geq 0
\end{aligned}
$$

b. $L = 48, D = 72, S = 30$
  Total cost = \$3780
c. No change
d. No change

24. a. 333.3, 0, 833.3; Risk = 14,666.7; Return = 18,000 or 9%
  b. 1000, 0, 0, 2500; Risk = 18,000; Return = 22,000 or 11%
  c. \$4000

26. a. Let M_1 = units of component 1 manufactured
M_2 = units of component 2 manufactured
M_3 = units of component 3 manufactured
P_1 = units of component 1 purchased
P_2 = units of component 2 purchased
P_3 = units of component 3 purchased

Min $4.50M_1 + 5.00M_2 + 2.75M_3 + 6.50P_1 + 8.80P_2 + 7.00P_3$
s.t.

$2M_1 + 3M_2 + 4M_3$	$\leq 21{,}600$	Production
$1M_1 + 1.5M_2 + 3M_3$	$\leq 15{,}000$	Assembly
$1.5M_1 + 2M_2 + 5M_3$	$\leq 18{,}000$	Testing/Packaging
$1M_1 + 1P_1$	$= 6{,}000$	Component 1
$1M_2 + 1P_2$	$= 4{,}000$	Component 2
$1M_3 + 1P_3 =$	$3{,}500$	Component 3

$M_1, M_2, M_3, P_1, P_2, P_3 \geq 0$

b.

Source	Component 1	Component 2	Component 3
Manufacture	2000	4000	1400
Purchase	4000		2100

Total Cost $73,550

c. Production: $54.36 per hour
Testing & Packaging: $ 7.50 per hour

d. Dual prices $= -\$7.969$; it would cost Benson $7.969 to add a unit of component 2

28. b. $G = 120{,}000$; $S = 30{,}000$; $M = 150{,}000$
c. 0.15 to 0.60; No Lower Limit to 0.122; 0.02 to 0.20
d. 4668
e. $G = 48{,}000$; $S = 192{,}000$; $M = 60{,}000$
f. The client's risk index and the amount of funds available

30. a. $L = 3, N = 7, W = 5, S = 5$
b. Each additional minute of broadcast time increases cost by $100
c. If local coverage is increased by 1 minute, total cost will increase by $100
d. If the time devoted to local and national news is increased by 1 minute, total cost will increase by $100
e. Increasing the sports by 1 minute will have no effect because the dual price is 0

32. a. Let P_1 = number of PT-100 battery packs produced at the Philippines plant
P_2 = number of PT-200 battery packs produced at the Philippines plant
P_3 = number of PT-300 battery packs produced at the Philippines plant
M_1 = number of PT-100 battery packs produced at the Mexico plant
M_2 = number of PT-200 battery packs produced at the Mexico plant
M_3 = number of PT-300 battery packs produced at the Mexico plant

Min $1.13P_1 + 1.16P_2 + 1.52P_3 + 1.08M_1 + 1.16M_2 + 1.25M_3$
s.t.

$P_1 +$		M_1		$= 200{,}000$
	$P_2 +$		M_2	$= 100{,}000$
	$P_3 +$		M_3	$= 150{,}000$
$P_1 + P_2$				$\leq 175{,}000$
		$M_1 +$	M_2	$\leq 160{,}000$
	P_3			$\leq 75{,}000$
			M_3	$\leq 100{,}000$

$P_1, P_2, P_3, M_1, M_2, M_3 \geq 0$

b. The optimal solution is as follows:

	Philippines	Mexico
PT-100	40,000	160,000
PT-200	100,000	0
PT-300	50,000	100,000

Total production and transportation cost is $535,000

c. The range of optimality for the objective function coefficient for P_1 shows a lower limit of $1.08; thus, the production and/or shipping cost would have to decrease by at least 5 cents per unit

d. The range of optimality for the objective function coefficient for M_1 shows a lower limit of $1.11; thus, the production and/or shipping cost would have to decrease by at least 5 cents per unit

Chapter 9

1. a. Let T = number of television advertisements
R = number of radio advertisements
N = number of newspaper advertisements

Max $100{,}000T + 18{,}000R + 40{,}000N$
s.t.

$2000T +$	$300R +$	$600N \leq 18{,}200$		Budget
T			≤ 10	Max TV
	R		≤ 20	Max radio
		$N \leq$	10	Max news
$-0.5T +$	$0.5R -$	$0.5N \leq$	0	Max 50% radio
$0.9T -$	$0.1R -$	$0.1N \geq$	0	Min 10% TV

$T, R, N \geq 0$

		Budget $
Solution:	$T = 4$	$\$ \ 8000$
	$R = 14$	4200
	$N = 10$	6000
		$\overline{\$18{,}200}$

Audience $= 1{,}052{,}000$

b. The dual price for the budget constraint is 51.30. Thus, a $100 increase in the budget should provide an increase in audience coverage of approximately 5130. The right-hand-side range for the budget constraint will show that this interpretation is correct.

2. a. $x_1 = 77.89, x_2 = 63.16, \$3284.21$
b. Department A $15.79; Department B $47.37
c. $x_1 = 87.21, x_2 = 65.12, \$3341.34$
Department A 10 hours; Department B 3.2 hours

4. a. $x_1 = 500, x_2 = 300, x_3 = 200, \$550$

  b. $\$0.55$

  c. Aroma, 75; Taste 84.4

  d. $-\$0.60$

6. 50 units of product 1; 0 units of product 2; 300 hours department A; 600 hours department B

8. Schedule 19 officers as follows:

3 begin at 8:00 A.M.; 3 begin at noon; 7 begin at 4:00 P.M.; 4 begin at midnight, 2 begin at 4:00 A.M.

9. a. Decision variables $A, P, M, H,$ and G represent the fraction or proportion of the total investment in each alternative

Max $0.073A + 0.103P + 0.064M + 0.075H + 0.045G$

s.t.

$$
\begin{array}{rrrrrl}
A + & P + & M + & H + & G = & 1 \\
0.5A + & 0.5P - & 0.5M - & 0.5H & & \leq 0 \\
-0.5A - & 0.5P + & 0.5M + & 0.5H & & \leq 0 \\
& & -0.25M - & 0.25H + & G \geq & 0 \\
-0.6A + & 0.4P & & & & \leq 0 \\
A, P, M, H, G \geq 0 & & & & &
\end{array}
$$

Objective function $= 0.079$; $A = 0.178$; $P = 0.267$; $M = 0.000$; $H = 0.444$; $G = 0.111$

  b. Multiplying $A, P, M, H,$ and G by the $\$100,000$ invested provides the following

Atlantic Oil	$ 17,800
Pacific Oil	26,700
Huber Steel	44,400
Government bonds	11,100
	$100,000

  c. $0.079(\$100,000) = \$7900$

  d. The marginal rate of return is 0.079

10. a. 40.9%, 14.5%, 14.5%, 30.0%

Annual return $= 5.4\%$

  b. 0.0%, 36.0%, 36.0%, 28.0%

Annual return $= 2.52\%$

  c. 75.0%, 0.0%, 15.0%, 10.0%

Annual return $= 8.2\%$

  b. Yes

12.

Week	Buy	Sell	Store
1	80,000	0	100,000
2	0	0	100,000
3	0	100,000	0
4	25,000	0	25,000

14. b.

Quarter	Production	Ending Inventory
1	4000	2100
2	3000	1100
3	2000	100
4	1900	500

15. Let x_{11} = gallons of crude 1 used to produce regular

         x_{12} = gallons of crude 1 used to produce high octane

         x_{21} = gallons of crude 2 used to produce regular

         x_{22} = gallons of crude 2 used to produce high octane

Min $0.10x_{11} + 0.10x_{12} + 0.15x_{21} + 0.15x_{22}$

s.t.

Each gallon of regular must have at least 40% A

$x_{11} + x_{21}$ = amount of regular produced

$0.4(x_{11} + x_{21})$ = amount of A required for regular

$0.2x_{11} + 0.50x_{21}$ = amount of A in $(x_{11} + x_{21})$ gallons of regular gas

$$\therefore 0.2x_{11} + 0.50x_{21} \geq 0.4x_{11} + 0.40x_{21}$$

$$\therefore -0.2x_{11} + 0.10x_{21} \geq 0$$

Each gallon of high octane can have at most 50% B

$x_{12} + x_{22}$ = amount high octane

$0.5(x_{12} + x_{22})$ = amount of B required for high octane

$0.60x_{12} + 0.30x_{22}$ = amount of B in $(x_{12} + x_{22})$ gallons of high octane

$$\therefore 0.60x_{12} + 0.30x_{22} \leq 0.5x_{12} + 0.5x_{22}$$

$$\therefore 0.1x_{12} - 0.2x_{22} \leq 0$$

$$x_{11} + x_{21} \geq 800,000$$

$$x_{12} + x_{22} \geq 500,000$$

$$x_{11}, x_{12}, x_{21}, x_{22} \geq 0$$

Optimal solution: $x_{11} = 266,667, x_{12} = 333,333, x_{21} = 533,333, x_{22} = 166,667$

Cost $= \$165,000$

16. x_i = number of 10-inch rolls processed by cutting alternative i

  a. $x_1 = 0, x_2 = 125, x_3 = 500, x_4 = 1500, x_5 = 0, x_6 = 0, x_7 = 0$; 2125 rolls with waste of 750 inches

  b. 2500 rolls with no waste; however, $1\frac{1}{2}$-inch size is overproduced by 3000 units

18. a. 5 Super, 2 Regular, and 3 Econo-Tankers

Total cost $\$583,000$; monthly operating cost $\$4650$

19. a. Let x_{11} = amount of men's model in month 1

         x_{21} = amount of women's model in month 1

         x_{12} = amount of men's model in month 2

         x_{22} = amount of women's model in month 2

         s_{11} = inventory of men's model at end of month 1

         s_{21} = inventory of women's model at end of month 1

         s_{12} = inventory of men's model at end of month 2

         s_{22} = inventory of women's model at end of month 2

Min $120x_{11} + 90x_{21} + 120x_{12} + 90x_{22} + 2.4s_{11} + 1.8s_{21} + 2.4s_{12} + 1.8s_{22}$

s.t.

$$
\left.
\begin{array}{rrrrl}
x_{11} - & s_{11} & & = & 130 \\
x_{21} - & s_{21} & & = & 95 \\
s_{11} + & x_{12} - & s_{12} & = & 200 \\
s_{21} + & x_{22} - & s_{22} & = & 150
\end{array}
\right\} \text{Satisfy demand}
$$

$$
\left.
\begin{array}{l}
s_{12} \geq 25 \\
s_{22} \geq 25
\end{array}
\right\} \text{Ending inventory requirement}
$$

Labor-hours: Men's $2.0 + 1.5 = 3.5$

              Women's $1.6 + 1.0 = 2.6$

$$
\left.
\begin{array}{l}
3.5x_{11} + 2.6x_{21} \geq 900 \\
3.5x_{11} + 2.6x_{21} \leq 1100 \\
3.5x_{11} + 2.6x_{21} - 3.5x_{12} - 2.6x_{22} \leq 100 \\
-3.5x_{11} - 2.6x_{21} + 3.5x_{12} + 2.6x_{22} \leq 100
\end{array}
\right\} \text{Labor smoothing}
$$

$$x_{11}, x_{12}, x_{21}, x_{22}, s_{11}, s_{12}, s_{21}, s_{22} \geq 0$$

Solution: $x_{11} = 193$; $x_{21} = 95$; $x_{12} = 162$; $x_{22} = 175$

Total cost = $67,156
Inventory levels: $s_{11} = 63$; $s_{12} = 25$; $s_{21} = 0$; $s_{22} = 25$
Labor levels: Previous 1000 hours
Month 1 922.25 hours
Month 2 1022.25 hours

b. To accommodate the new policy, the right-hand sides of the four labor-smoothing constraints must be changed to 950, 1050, 50, and 50, respectively; the new total cost is $67,175

20. Produce 10,250 units in March, 10,250 units in April, and 12,000 units in May

22. 5,515,887 sq. in. of waste
Machine 3: 492 minutes

24. Investment strategy: 45.8% of A and 100% of B
Objective function = $4340.40
Savings/Loan schedule

	Period			
	1	**2**	**3**	**4**
Savings	242.11	—	—	341.04
Funds from loan	—	200.00	127.58	—

26. b. Solution does not indicate that General Hospital is relatively inefficient
c. General Hospital

28. c. No; E = 1 indicates that all the resources used by Hospital E are required to produce the outputs of Hospital E
d. Hospital E

30. a. Newark
b. Five ODIFs change: $PMQ = 23$; $POQ = 43$; $NMQ = 56$; $CMQ = 32$; and $COQ = 46$; the allocations for the other ODIFs remain the same as in the original solution
c. Four ODIFs change: $POQ = 45$; $NMQ = 56$; $CMQ = 37$; and $COQ = 44$; the allocations for the other ODIFs remain the same as in the original solution
d. COY, with a bid price of $443

32. c.

Type	Value
Convention/two-night package	36
Convention/Friday only	12
Convention/Saturday only	15
Regular/Two-night package	20
Regular/Friday only	28
Regular/Saturday only	25

d. $50

Chapter 10

1.

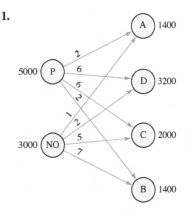

2. a. Let x_{11} = amount shipped from Jefferson City to Des Moines
x_{12} = amount shipped from Jefferson City to Kansas City
.
.
.
x_{23} = amount shipped from Omaha to St. Louis

Min $14x_{11} + 9x_{12} + 7x_{13} + 8x_{21} + 10x_{22} + 5x_{23}$
s.t.
$$
\begin{aligned}
x_{11} + x_{12} + x_{13} && \le 30 \\
x_{21} + x_{22} + x_{23} && \le 20 \\
x_{11} + x_{21} && = 25 \\
x_{12} + x_{22} && = 15 \\
x_{13} + x_{23} && = 10 \\
x_{11}, x_{12}, x_{13}, x_{21}, x_{22}, x_{23} \ge 0
\end{aligned}
$$

b.

Optimal Solution	Amount	Cost
Jefferson City–Des Moines	5	70
Jefferson City–Kansas City	15	135
Jefferson City–St. Louis	10	70
Omaha–Des Moines	20	160
	Total	435

4. b. $x_{12} = 300, x_{21} = 100, x_{22} = 100, x_{23} = 300, x_{31} = 100$
Cost = 10,400

6. b.

Seattle–Denver	4000	Seattle–Los Angeles	5000
Columbus–Mobile	4000	New York–Pittsburgh	3000
New York–Mobile	1000	New York–Los Angeles	1000
New York–Washington	3000		

Cost = $150,000

c.

Seattle–Denver	4000	Seattle–Los Angeles	5000
Columbus–Mobile	5000	New York–Pittsburgh	4000
New York–Los Angeles	1000	New York–Washington	3000

Cost actually decreases by $9000

8. The network model, the linear programming formulation and the optimal solution are shown. Note that the third constraint corresponds to the dummy origin; the variables x_{31}, x_{32}, x_{33}, and x_{34} are the amounts shipped out of the dummy origin and do not appear in the objective function since they are given a coefficient of zero

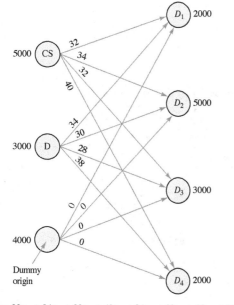

Max $32x_{11} + 34x_{12} + 32x_{13} + 40x_{14} + 34x_{21} + 30x_{22} + 28x_{23} + 38x_{24}$
s.t.

$$
\begin{aligned}
x_{11} + x_{12} + x_{13} + x_{14} &\le 5000 \\
x_{21} + x_{22} + x_{23} + x_{24} &\le 3000 \\
x_{31} + x_{32} + x_{33} + x_{34} &\le 4000 \\
x_{11} \quad\quad + x_{21} \quad\quad + x_{31} &= 2000 \\
x_{12} \quad\quad + x_{22} \quad\quad + x_{32} &= 5000 \\
x_{13} \quad\quad + x_{23} \quad\quad + x_{33} &= 3000 \\
x_{14} \quad\quad + x_{24} \quad\quad + x_{34} &= 2000 \\
x_{ij} \ge 0 \quad \text{for all } i, j
\end{aligned}
$$

Optimal Solution	Units	Cost
Clifton Springs-D_2	4,000	$136,000
Clifton Springs-D_4	1,000	40,000
Danville-D_1	2,000	68,000
Danville-D_4	1,000	38,000
	Total	$282,000

Customer 2 demand has a shortfall of 1000; customer 3 demand of 3000 is not satisfied

10. 1–A 300; 1–C 1200; 2–A 1200; 3–A 500; 3–B 500

12. a.

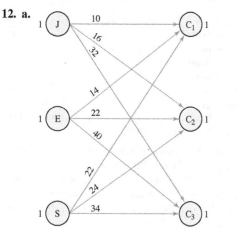

b.

Min $10x_{11} + 16x_{12} + 32x_{13} + 14x_{21} + 22x_{22} + 40x_{23} + 22x_{31} + 24x_{32} + 34x_{33}$
s.t.

$$
\begin{aligned}
x_{11} + x_{12} + x_{13} &\le 1 \\
x_{21} + x_{22} + x_{23} &\le 1 \\
x_{31} + x_{32} + x_{33} &\le 1 \\
x_{11} \quad\quad + x_{21} \quad\quad + x_{31} &= 1 \\
x_{12} \quad\quad + x_{22} \quad\quad + x_{32} &= 1 \\
x_{13} \quad\quad + x_{23} \quad\quad + x_{33} &= 1 \\
x_{ij} \ge 0 \quad \text{for all } i, j
\end{aligned}
$$

Solution $x_{12} = 1, x_{21} = 1, x_{33} = 1$; total completion time = 64

14. b.

Green:	Job 1	$ 26
Brown:	Job 2	34
Red:	Job 3	38
Blue:	Job 4	39
White:	Job 5	25
	Total Cost	$162

16. b. Toy to 2, Auto Parts to 4, Housewares to 3, Video to 1

18. a. Plano: Kansas City and Dallas
Flagstaff: Los Angeles
Springfield: Chicago, Columbus, and Atlanta
Boulder: Newark and Denver
Cost = $216,000
b. Nashville
c. Columbus is switched from Springfield to Nashville
Cost = $227,000

20. A to MS, B to Ph.D., C to MBA, D to undergrad
Maximum total rating = 13.3

22. a.

	Supplier					
Division	1	2	3	4	5	6
1	614	660	534	680	590	630
2	603	639	702	693	693	630
3	865	830	775	850	900	930
4	532	553	511	581	595	553
5	720	648	684	693	657	747

b. Optimal solution:

Supplier 1–Division 2	$ 603
Supplier 2–Division 5	648
Supplier 3–Division 3	775
Supplier 5–Division 1	590
Supplier 6–Division 4	553
Total	$3169

23. a.

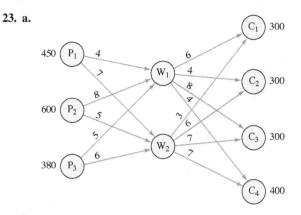

b.

$$\text{Min } 4x_{14}+7x_{15}+8x_{24}+5x_{25}+5x_{34}+6x_{35}+6x_{46}+4x_{47}+8x_{48}+4x_{49}+3x_{56}+6x_{57}+7x_{58}+7x_{59}$$

s.t.

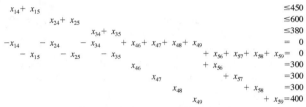

c.

Plant	Warehouse 1	Warehouse 2
1	450	—
2	—	600
3	250	—

Total cost = $11,850

Warehouse	Customer 1	Customer 2	Customer 3	Customer 4
1	—	300	—	400
2	300	—	300	—

24. c. $x_{14} = 320, x_{25} = 600, x_{47} = 300, x_{49} = 20, x_{56} = 300,$
$x_{58} = 300, x_{39} = 380$
Cost = $11,220

26. c. Note: Augusta: 1, Tupper Lake: 2, Albany: 3, Portsmouth: 4, Boston: 5, New York: 6, Philadelphia: 7

Variable	Value	Variable	Value
x_{13}	50	x_{36}	0
x_{14}	250	x_{37}	150
x_{23}	100	x_{45}	150
x_{24}	0	x_{46}	100
x_{35}	0	x_{47}	0

Objective function = 4300

28.

Optimal Solution	Units Shipped	Cost
Muncie–Cincinnati	1	6
Cincinnati–Concord	3	84
Brazil–Louisville	6	18
Louisville–Macon	2	88
Louisville–Greenwood	4	136
Xenia–Cincinnati	5	15
Cincinnati–Chatham	3	72
	Total	419

Two rail cars must be held at Muncie until a buyer is found

32. c. Regular-month 1: 275; overtime-month 1: 25; inventory at end of month 1: 150
Regular-month 2: 200; overtime-month 2: 50; inventory at end of month 2: 150
Regular-month 3: 100; overtime-month 3: 50; inventory at end of month 3: 0

Chapter 11

2. a.

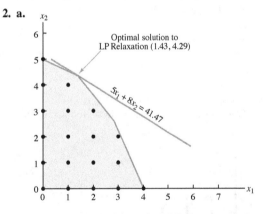

b. The optimal solution to the LP Relaxation is given by
$x_1 = 1.43, x_2 = 4.29$ with an objective function value
of 41.47. Rounding down gives the feasible integer solution $x_1 = 1, x_2 = 4$; its value is 37

c.

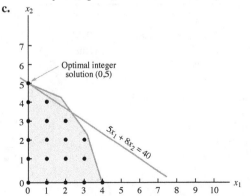

The optimal solution is given by $x_1 = 0$, $x_2 = 5$; its value is 40. It is not the same solution as found by rounding down; it provides a 3-unit increase in the value of the objective function

4. a. $x_1 = 3.67, x_2 = 0$; Value $= 36.7$
    Rounded: $x_1 = 3, x_2 = 0$; Value $= 30$
    Lower bound $= 30$; Upper bound $= 36.7$
b. $x_1 = 3, x_2 = 2$; Value $= 36$
c. Alternative optimal solutions: $x_1 = 0, x_2 = 5$
                          $x_1 = 2, x_2 = 4$

5. a. The feasible mixed-integer solutions are indicated by the boldface vertical lines in the graph

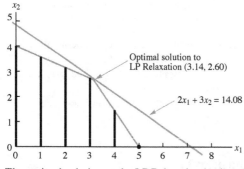

b. The optimal solution to the LP Relaxation is given by $x_1 = 3.14, x_2 = 2.60$; its value is 14.08
    Rounding down the value of x_1 to find a feasible mixed-integer solution yields $x_1 = 3, x_2 = 2.60$ with a value of 13.8; this solution is clearly not optimal; with $x_1 = 3$, x_2 can be made larger without violating the constraints
c. The optimal solution to the MILP is given by $x_1 = 3, x_2 = 2.67$; its value is 14 as shown in the following figure

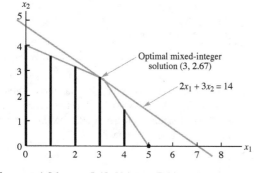

6. b. $x_1 = 1.96, x_2 = 5.48$; Value $= 7.44$
    Rounded: $x_1 = 1.96, x_2 = 5$; Value $= 6.96$
    Lower bound $= 6.96$; Upper bound $= 7.44$
c. $x_1 = 1.29, x_2 = 6$; Value $= 7.29$

7. a. $x_1 + x_3 + x_5 + x_6 = 2$
b. $x_3 - x_5 = 0$
c. $x_1 + x_4 = 1$
d. $x_4 \leq x_1$
    $x_4 \leq x_3$

e. $x_4 \leq x_1$
    $x_4 \leq x_3$
    $x_4 \geq x_1 + x_3 - 1$

8. a. $x_3 = 1, x_4 = 1, x_6 = 1$; Value $= 17{,}500$
b. Add $x_1 + x_2 \leq 1$
c. Add $x_3 - x_4 = 0$

10. b. Choose locations B and E

12. a. $P \leq 15 + 15 Y_P$
    $D \leq 15 + 15 Y_D$
    $J \leq 15 + 15 Y_J$
    $Y_P + Y_D + Y_J \leq 1$
b. $P = 15, D = 15, J = 30$
    $Y_P = 0, Y_D = 0, Y_J = 1$; Value $= 50$

13. a. Add the following multiple-choice constraint to the problem
    $y_1 + y_2 = 1$
    New optimal solution: $y_1 = 1$, $y_3 = 1$, $x_{12} = 10$, $x_{31} = 30, x_{52} = 10, x_{53} = 20$
    Value $= 940$
b. Because one plant is already located in St. Louis, it is only necessary to add the following constraint to the model
    $y_3 + y_4 \leq 1$
    New optimal solution: $y_4 = 1, x_{42} = 20, x_{43} = 20, x_{51} = 30$
    Value $= 860$

14. b. Modernize plants 1 and 3 or plants 4 and 5
d. Modernize plants 1 and 3

16. b. Use all part-time employees
    Bring on as follows: 9:00 A.M.–6, 11:00 A.M.–2, 12:00 noon–6, 1:00 P.M.–1, 3:00 P.M.–6
    Cost $= \$672$
c. Same as in part (b)
d. New solution is to bring on 1 full-time employee at 9:00 A.M., 4 more at 11:00 A.M. and part-time employees as follows:
    9:00 A.M.–5, 12:00 noon–5, and 3:00 P.M.–2

18. a. $52, 49, 36, 83, 39, 70, 79, 59$
b. Thick crust, cheese blend, chunky sauce, medium sausage. Six of eight consumers will prefer this pizza (75%)

20. a. New objective function: Min $25x_1 + 40x_2 + 40x_3 + 40x_4 + 25x_5$
b. $x_4 = x_5 = 1$; modernize the Ohio and California plants
c. Add the constraint $x_2 + x_3 = 1$
d. $x_1 = x_3 = 1$

22. $x_1 + x_2 + x_3 = 3y_1 + 5y_2 + 7y_3$
    $y_1 + y_2 + y_3 = 1$

24. a. $x_{111}, x_{112}, x_{121}$
b. $x_{111} + x_{112} + x_{121} \leq 1$
c. $x_{531} + x_{532} + x_{533} + x_{541} + x_{542} + x_{543} + x_{551} + x_{552} + x_{561} \leq 1$
d. Only two screens are available
e. $x_{213} + x_{222} + x_{231} + x_{422} + x_{431} + x_{531} + x_{532} + x_{533} + x_{631} + x_{632} + x_{633} \leq 2$

Chapter 12

2.

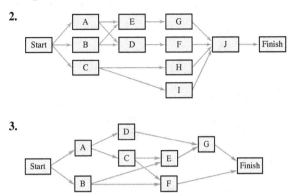

3.

4. a. A–D–G
  b. No; Time = 15 months

6. a. Critial path: A–D–F–H
  b. 22 weeks
  c. No, it is a critical activity
  d. Yes, 2 weeks
  e. Schedule for activity E:

Earliest start	3
Latest start	4
Earliest finish	10
Latest finish	11

8. b. B–C–E–F–H
  d. Yes, time = 49 weeks

10. a.

Activity	Optimistic	Most Probable	Pessimistic	Expected Times	Variance
A	4	5.0	6	5.00	0.11
B	8	9.0	10	9.00	0.11
C	7	7.5	11	8.00	0.44
D	7	9.0	10	8.83	0.25
E	6	7.0	9	7.17	0.25
F	5	6.0	7	6.00	0.11

  b. Critical activities: B–D–F
  Expected project completion time: 9.00 + 8.83 + 6.00 = 23.83
  Variance of projection completion time: 0.11 + 0.25 + 0.11 = 0.47

12. a. A–D–H–I
  b. 25.66 days
  c. 0.2578

13.

Activity	Expected Time	Variance
A	5	0.11
B	3	0.03
C	7	0.11
D	6	0.44
E	7	0.44
F	3	0.11
G	10	0.44
H	8	1.78

From Problem 6, A–D–F–H is the critical path, so
$E(T) = 5 + 6 + 3 + 8 = 22$

$\sigma^2 = 0.11 + 0.44 + 0.11 + 1.78 = 2.44$

$$z = \frac{Time - E(T)}{\sigma} = \frac{Time - 22}{\sqrt{2.44}}$$

  a. Time = 21: $z = -0.64$ Area 0.2389
  $P(21 \text{ weeks}) = 0.500 - 0.2389 = 0.2611$

  b. Time = 22: $z = 0$ Area 0.0000
  $P(22 \text{ weeks}) = 0.5000$

  c. Time = 25: $z = +1.92$ Area 0.4726
  $P(25 \text{ weeks}) = 0.5000 + 0.4726 = 0.9726$

14. a. A–C–E–G–H
  b. 52 weeks (1 year)
  c. 0.0174
  d. 0.0934
  e. 10 month doubtful
  13 month very likely
  Estimate 12 months (1 year)

16. a.

$E(T)$	Variance
16	3.92
13	2.03
10	1.27

  b. 0.9783, approximately 1.00, approximately 1.00

18. c. A–B–D–G–H–I, 14.17 weeks
  d. 0.0951, yes

20. b. Crash B(1 week), D(2 weeks), E(1 week), F(1 week), G(1 week)
  Total cost = $2427
  c. All activities are critical

21. a.

Activity	Earliest Start	Latest Start	Earliest Finish	Latest Finish	Slack	Critical Activity
A	0	0	3	3	0	Yes
B	0	1	2	3	1	
C	3	3	8	8	0	Yes
D	2	3	7	8	1	
E	8	8	14	14	0	Yes
F	8	10	10	12	2	
G	10	12	12	14	2	

Critical Path: A–C–E

Project completion time $= t_A + t_C + t_E = 3 + 5 + 6 = 14$ days

b. Total cost = $8400

22. a.

Activity	Max Crash Days	Crash Cost/Day
A	1	600
B	1	700
C	2	400
D	2	400
E	2	500
F	1	400
G	1	500

Min $600Y_A + 700Y_B + 400Y_C + 400Y_D + 500Y_E + 400Y_F + 400Y_G$

s.t.

$$X_A + Y_A \geq 3$$
$$X_B + Y_B \geq 2$$
$$-X_A + X_C + Y_C \geq 5$$
$$-X_B + X_D + Y_D \geq 5$$
$$-X_C + X_E + Y_E \geq 6$$
$$-X_D + X_E + Y_E \geq 6$$
$$-X_C + X_F + Y_F \geq 2$$
$$-X_D + X_F + Y_F \geq 2$$
$$-X_F + X_G + Y_G \geq 2$$
$$-X_E + X_{FIN} \geq 0$$
$$-X_G + X_{FIN} \geq 0$$
$$X_{FIN} \leq 12$$
$$Y_A \leq 1$$
$$Y_B \leq 1$$
$$Y_C \leq 2$$
$$Y_D \leq 2$$
$$Y_E \leq 2$$
$$Y_F \leq 1$$
$$Y_G \leq 1$$

All $X, Y \geq 0$

b. Solution of the linear programming model in part (a) shows

Activity	Crash	Crashing Cost
C	1 day	$400
E	1 day	500
	Total	$900

c. Total cost = Normal cost + Crashing cost
= $8400 + $900 = $9300

24. c. A–B–C–F, 31 weeks

d. Crash A(2 weeks), B(2 weeks), C(1 week), D(1 week), E(1 week)

e. All activities are critical

f. $112,500

Chapter 13

1. a. $Q^* = \sqrt{\dfrac{2DC_0}{C_h}} = \sqrt{\dfrac{2(3600)(20)}{0.25(3)}} = 438.18$

b. $r = dm = \dfrac{3600}{250}(5) = 72$

c. $T = \dfrac{250Q^*}{D} = \dfrac{250(438.18)}{3600} = 30.43$ days

d. $TC = \dfrac{1}{2}QC_h + \dfrac{D}{Q}C_0$

$= \dfrac{1}{2}(438.18)(0.25)(3) + \dfrac{3600}{438.18}(20) = \$328.63$

2. $164.32 for each; Total cost = $328.64

4. a. 1095.45

b. 240

c. 22.82 days

d. $273.86 for each; Total cost = $547.72

6. a. 15.95

b. $2106

c. 15.04

d. 16.62 days

8. $Q^* = 11.73$, use 12

5 classes per year

$225,200

10. $Q^* = 1414.21$

$T = 28.28$ days

Production runs of 7.07 days

12. a. 1500

b. 4; 3 month cycle time

c. Change to $Q^* = 1500$

d. Savings = $12,510

13. a. $Q^* = \sqrt{\dfrac{2DC_0}{(1 - D/P)C_h}}$

$= \sqrt{\dfrac{2(7200)(150)}{(1 - 7200/25,000)(0.18)(14.50)}} = 1078.12$

b. Number of production runs $= \dfrac{D}{Q^*} = \dfrac{7200}{1078.12} = 6.68$

c. $T = \dfrac{250Q}{D} = \dfrac{250(1078.12)}{7200} = 37.43$ days

d. Production run length $= \dfrac{Q}{P/250}$

$= \dfrac{1078.12}{25,000/250} = 10.78$ days

e. Maximum inventory $= \left(1 - \dfrac{D}{P}\right)Q$

$$= \left(1 - \dfrac{7200}{25,000}\right)(1078.12)$$

$$= 767.62$$

f. Holding cost $= \dfrac{1}{2}\left(1 - \dfrac{D}{P}\right)QC_h$

$$= \dfrac{1}{2}\left(1 - \dfrac{7200}{25,000}\right)(1078.12)(0.18)(14.50)$$

$$= \$1001.74$$

Ordering cost $= \dfrac{D}{Q}C_0 = \dfrac{7200}{1078.12}(150) = \$1001.74$

Total cost $= \$2003.48$

g. $r = dm = \left(\dfrac{D}{250}\right)m = \dfrac{7200}{250}(15) = 432$

14. New $Q^* = 4509$

15. a. $Q^* = \sqrt{\dfrac{2DC_0}{C_h}\left(\dfrac{C_h + C_b}{C_b}\right)}$

$$= \sqrt{\dfrac{2(12,000)(25)}{0.50}\left(\dfrac{0.50 + 5}{0.50}\right)} = 1148.91$$

b. $S^* = Q^*\left(\dfrac{C_h}{C_h + C_b}\right) = 1148.91\left(\dfrac{0.50}{0.50 + 5}\right) = 104.45$

c. Max inventory $= Q^* - S^* = 1044.46$

d. $T = \dfrac{250Q^*}{D} = \dfrac{250(1148.91)}{12,000} = 23.94$ days

e. Holding $= \dfrac{(Q - S)^2}{2Q}C_h = \$237.38$

Ordering $= \dfrac{D}{Q}C_0 = \$261.12$

Backorder $= \dfrac{S^2}{2Q}C_b = \$23.74$

Total cost $= \$522.24$

The total cost for the EOQ model in Problem 4 was $547.72; allowing backorders reduces the total cost

16. $135.55; r = dm - S$; less than

18. $64, 24.44$

20. $Q^* = 100$; Total cost $= \$3,601.50$

21. $Q = \sqrt{\dfrac{2DC_0}{C_h}}$

$Q_1 = \sqrt{\dfrac{2(500)(40)}{0.20(10)}} = 141.42$

$Q_2 = \sqrt{\dfrac{2(500)(40)}{0.20(9.7)}} = 143.59$

Because Q_1 is over its limit of 99 units, Q_1 cannot be optimal (see Problem 23); use $Q_2 = 143.59$ as the optimal order quantity

Total cost $= \dfrac{1}{2}QC_h + \dfrac{D}{Q}C_0 + DC$

$$= 139.28 + 139.28 + 4850.00 = \$5128.56$$

22. $Q^* = 300$; Savings $= \$480$

24. a. 500

b. 580.4

25. a. $c_0 = 80 - 50 = 30$

$c_u = 125 - 80 = 45$

$$P(D \le Q^*) = \dfrac{c_u}{c_u + c_0} = \dfrac{45}{45 + 30} = 0.60$$

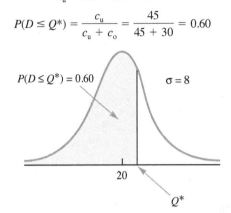

For an area of 0.60 below Q^*, $z = 0.25$
$Q^* = 20 + 0.25(8) = 22$

b. $P(\text{Sell all}) = P(D \ge Q^*) = 1 - 0.60 = 0.40$

26. a. $150

b. $240 - $150 = $90

c. 47

d. 0.625

28. a. 440

b. 0.60

c. 710

d. $c_u = \$17$

29. a. $r = dm = (200/250)15 = 12$

b. $\dfrac{D}{Q} = \dfrac{200}{25} = 8$ orders/year

The limit of 1 stock-out per year means that
$P(\text{Stock-out/cycle}) = 1/8 = 0.125$

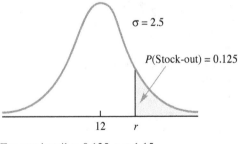

For area in tail $= 0.125$, $z = 1.15$

$$z = \dfrac{r - 12}{2.5} = 1.15$$

or

$$r = 12 + 1.15(2.5) = 14.875 \approx 15$$

c. Safety stock $= 3$ units
Added cost $= 3(\$5) = \$15$/year

30. a. 13.68 (14)
   b. 17.83 (18)
   c. 2, $10; 6, $30

32. a. 31.62
   b. 19.86 (20); 0.2108
   c. 5, $15

33. a. $1/52 = 0.0192$
   b. $M = \mu + z\sigma = 60 + 2.07(12) = 85$
   c. $M = 35 + (0.9808)(85 - 35) = 84$

34. a. 243
   b. 93, $54.87
   c. 613
   d. 163, $96.17
   e. Yes, added cost only $41.30 per year
   f. Yes, added cost would be $4130 per year

36. a. 40
   b. 62.25; 7.9
   c. 54
   d. 36

Chapter 14

2. a. 0.4512
   b. 0.6988
   c. 0.3012

4. 0.3333, 0.2222, 0.1481, 0.0988; 0.1976

5. a. $P_0 = 1 - \dfrac{\lambda}{\mu} = 1 - \dfrac{10}{12} = 0.1667$

   b. $L_q = \dfrac{\lambda^2}{\mu(\mu - \lambda)} = \dfrac{10^2}{12(12 - 10)} = 4.1667$

   c. $W_q = \dfrac{L_q}{\lambda} = 0.4167$ hour (25 minutes)

   d. $W = W_q + \dfrac{1}{\mu} = 0.5$ hour (30 minutes)

   e. $P_w = \dfrac{\lambda}{\mu} = \dfrac{10}{12} = 0.8333$

6. a. 0.3750
   b. 1.0417
   c. 0.8333 minutes (50 seconds)
   d. 0.6250
   e. Yes

8. 0.20, 3.2, 4, 3.2, 4, 0.80
   Slightly poorer service

10. a. New: 0.3333, 1.3333, 2, 0.6667, 1, 0.6667
      Experienced: 0.50, 0.50, 1, 0.25, 0.50, 0.50
   b. New $74; experienced $50; hire experienced

11. a. $\lambda = 2.5$; $\mu = \dfrac{60}{10} = 6$ customers per hour

   $L_q = \dfrac{\lambda^2}{\mu(\mu - \lambda)} = \dfrac{(2.5)^2}{6(6 - 2.5)} = 0.2976$

$L = L_q + \dfrac{\lambda}{\mu} = 0.7143$

$W_q = \dfrac{L_q}{\lambda} = 0.1190$ hours (7.14 minutes)

$W = W_q + \dfrac{1}{\mu} = 0.2857$ hours

$P_w = \dfrac{\lambda}{\mu} = \dfrac{2.5}{6} = 0.4167$

b. No; $W_q = 7.14$ minutes; firm should increase the service rate (μ) for the consultant or hire a second consultant

c. $\mu = \dfrac{60}{8} = 7.5$ customers per hour

$L_q = \dfrac{\lambda^2}{\mu(\mu - \lambda)} = \dfrac{(2.5)^2}{7.5(7.5 - 2.5)} = 0.1667$

$W_q = \dfrac{L_q}{\lambda} = 0.0667$ hour (4 minutes)

The service goal is being met

12. a. 0.25, 2.25, 3, 0.15 hours, 0.20 hours, 0.75
   b. The service needs improvement

14. a. 8
   b. 0.3750
   c. 1.0417
   d. 12.5 minutes
   e. 0.6250
   f. Add a second consultant

16. a. 0.50
   b. 0.50
   c. 0.10 hours (6 minutes)
   d. 0.20 hours (12 minutes)
   e. Yes, $W_q = 6$ minutes is most likely acceptable for a marina

18. a. $k = 2$; $\lambda/\mu = 5.4/3 = 1.8$; $P_0 = 0.0526$

$L_q = \dfrac{(\lambda/\mu)^2 \lambda\mu}{(k - 1)!(2\mu - \lambda)^2} P_0$

$= \dfrac{(1.8)^2(5.4)(3)}{(2 - 1)!(6 - 5.4)^2}(0.0526) = 7.67$

$L = L_q + \lambda/\mu = 7.67 + 1.8 = 9.47$

$W_q = \dfrac{L_q}{\lambda} = \dfrac{7.67}{5.4} = 1.42$ minutes

$W = W_q + 1/\mu = 1.42 + 0.33 = 1.75$ minutes

$P_w = \dfrac{1}{k!}\left(\dfrac{\lambda}{\mu}\right)^k \left(\dfrac{k\mu}{k\mu - \lambda}\right) P_0$

$= \dfrac{1}{2!}(1.8)^2 \left(\dfrac{6}{6 - 5.4}\right) 0.0526 = 0.8526$

b. $L_q = 7.67$; Yes
c. $W = 1.75$ minutes

20. a. Use $k = 2$
      $W = 3.7037$ minutes
      $L = 4.4444$
      $P_w = 0.7111$

b. For $k = 3$
   $W = 7.1778$ minutes
   $L = 15.0735$ customers
   $P_N = 0.8767$
   Expand post office

21. From Problem 11, a service time of 8 minutes has $\mu = 60/8 = 7.5$

$$L_q = \frac{\lambda^2}{\mu(\mu - \lambda)} = \frac{(2.5)^2}{7.5(7.5 - 2.5)} = 0.1667$$

$$L = L_q + \frac{\lambda}{\mu} = 0.50$$

Total cost $= \$25L + \$16$
$\qquad = 25(0.50) + 16 = \$28.50$

Two channels: $\lambda = 2.5; \mu = 60/10 = 6$
With $P_0 = 0.6552$,

$$L_q = \frac{(\lambda/\mu)^2 \lambda \mu}{1!(2\mu - \lambda)^2} P_0 = 0.0189$$

$$L = L_q + \frac{\lambda}{\mu} = 0.4356$$

Total cost $= 25(0.4356) + 2(16) = \$42.89$

Use one consultant with an 8-minute service time

22.

Characteristic	A	B	C
a. P_0	0.2000	0.5000	0.4286
b. L_q	3.2000	0.5000	0.1524
c. L	4.0000	1.0000	0.9524
d. W_q	0.1333	0.0208	0.0063
e. W	0.1667	0.0417	0.0397
f. P_w	0.8000	0.5000	0.2286

The two-channel System C provides the best service

24. a. $0.0466, 0.05$
   b. 1.4
   c. $11:00$ A.M.

25. $\lambda = 4, W = 10$ minutes
   a. $\mu = \frac{1}{2} = 0.5$
   b. $W_q = W - 1/\mu = 10 - 1/0.5 = 8$ minutes
   c. $L = \lambda W = 4(10) = 40$

26. a. $0.2668, 10$ minutes, 0.6667
   b. $0.0667, 7$ minutes, 0.4669
   c. $\$25.33; \$33.34;$ one-channel

27. a. $\frac{2}{8}$ hours $= 0.25$ per hour
   b. $1/3.2$ hours $= 0.3125$ per hour
   c. $L_q = \dfrac{\lambda^2 \sigma^2 + (\lambda/\mu)^2}{2(1 - \lambda/\mu)}$

$$= \frac{(0.25)^2(2)^2 + (0.25/0.3125)^2}{2(1 - 0.25/0.3125)} = 2.225$$

   d. $W_q = \dfrac{L_q}{\lambda} = \dfrac{2.225}{0.25} = 8.9$ hours

e. $W = W_q + \dfrac{1}{\mu} = 8.9 + \dfrac{1}{0.3125} = 12.1$ hours

f. Same as $P_w = \dfrac{\lambda}{\mu} = \dfrac{0.25}{0.3125} = 0.80$

   80% of the time the welder is busy

28. a. $10, 9.6$
   b. Design A with $\mu = 10$
   c. $0.05, 0.01$
   d. A: $0.5, 0.3125, 0.8125, 0.0625, 0.1625, 0.5$
      B: $0.4792, 0.2857, 0.8065, 0.0571, 0.1613, 0.5208$
   e. Design B has slightly less waiting time

30. a. $\lambda = 42; \mu = 20$

i	$(\lambda/\mu)^i/i!$
0	1.0000
1	2.1000
2	2.2050
3	1.5435
Total	6.8485

j	P_j	
0	1/6.8485	$= 0.1460$
1	2.1/6.8485	$= 0.3066$
2	2.2050/6.8485	$= 0.3220$
3	1.5435/6.8485	$= 0.2254$
		1.0000

   b. 0.2254
   c. $L = \lambda/\mu(1 - P_k) = 42/20(1 - 0.2254) = 1.6267$
   d. Four lines will be necessary; the probability of denied access is 0.1499

32. a. 31.03%
   b. 27.59%
   c. $0.2759, 0.1092, 0.0351$
   d. $3, 10.92\%$

34. $N = 5; \quad \lambda = 0.025; \quad \mu = 0.20; \quad \lambda/\mu = 0.125$
   a.

n	$\dfrac{N!}{(N - n)!}\left(\dfrac{\lambda}{\mu}\right)^n$
0	1.0000
1	0.6250
2	0.3125
3	0.1172
4	0.0293
5	0.0037
Total	2.0877

$$P_0 = 1/2.0877 = 0.4790$$

b. $L_q = N - \left(\dfrac{\lambda + \mu}{\lambda}\right)(1 - P_0)$

$\quad = 5 - \left(\dfrac{0.225}{0.025}\right)(1 - 0.4790) = 0.3110$

c. $L = L_q + (1 - P_0) = 0.3110 + (1 - 0.4790)$
$\quad = 0.8321$

d. $W_q = \dfrac{L_q}{(N - L)\lambda} = \dfrac{0.3110}{(5 - 0.8321)(0.025)}$
$\quad = 2.9854$ minutes

e. $W = W_q + \dfrac{1}{\mu} = 2.9854 + \dfrac{1}{0.20} = 7.9854$ minutes

f. Trips/day = (8 hours)(60 minutes/hour)(λ)
$\quad = (8)(60)(0.025) = 12$ trips
Time at copier: $12 \times 7.9854 = 95.8$ minutes/day
Wait time at copier: $12 \times 2.9854 = 35.8$ minutes/day

g. Yes, five assistants $\times 35.8 = 179$ minutes (3 hours/day),
so 3 hours per day are lost to waiting
$(35.8/480)(100) = 7.5\%$ of each assistant's day is spent
waiting for the copier

Chapter 15

2. a. c = variable cost per unit
x = demand
Profit = $(50 - c)x - 30,000$

b. Base: Profit = $(50 - 20)1200 - 30,000 = 6,000$
Worst: Profit = $(50 - 24)300 - 30,000 = -22,200$
Best: Profit = $(50 - 16)2100 - 30,000 = 41,400$

c. Simulation will be helpful in estimating the probability
of a loss

4. a.

Number of New Accounts	Interval
0	0.00 but less than 0.01
1	0.01 but less than 0.05
2	0.05 but less than 0.15
3	0.15 but less than 0.40
4	0.40 but less than 0.80
5	0.80 but less than 0.95
6	0.95 but less than 1.00

b. 4, 3, 3, 5, 2, 6, 4, 4, 4, 2
37 new accounts

c. First-year commission = $185,000
Cost of 10 seminars = $35,000
Yes

5. a.

Stock Price Change	Interval
-2	0.00 but less than 0.05
-1	0.05 but less than 0.15
0	0.15 but less than 0.40

Stock Price Change	Interval
+1	0.40 but less than 0.60
+2	0.60 but less than 0.80
+3	0.80 but less than 0.90
+4	0.90 but less than 1.00

b. Beginning price $39
0.1091 indicates −1 change; $38
0.9407 indicates +4 change; $42
0.1941 indicates 0 change; $42
0.8083 indicates +3 change; $45 (ending price)

6. a. 0.00–0.83, 0.83–0.89, 0.89–0.94, 0.94–0.96, 0.96–0.98,
0.98–0.99, 0.99–1.00

b. 4 claims paid; Total = $22,000

8. a. Atlanta wins each game if random number is in interval
0.00–0.60, 0.00–0.55, 0.00–0.48, 0.00–0.45, 0.00–0.48,
0.00–0.55, 0.00–0.50

b. Atlanta wins games 1, 2, 4, and 6
Atlanta wins series 4 to 2

c. Repeat many times; record % of Atlanta wins

9. a. Base-case based on most likely;
Time = $6 + 5 + 14 + 8 = 33$ weeks
Worst: Time = $8 + 7 + 18 + 10 = 43$ weeks
Best: Time = $5 + 3 + 10 + 8 = 26$ weeks

b. 0.1778 for A: 5 weeks
0.9617 for B: 7 weeks
0.6849 for C: 14 weeks
0.4503 for D: 8 weeks; Total = 34 weeks

c. Simulation will provide an estimate of the probability
of 35 weeks or less

10. a.

Hand Value	Interval
17	0.0000 but less than 0.1654
18	0.1654 but less than 0.2717
19	0.2717 but less than 0.3780
20	0.3780 but less than 0.4797
21	0.4797 but less than 0.5769
Broke	0.5769 but less than 1.0000

b, c, & d. Dealer wins 13 hands, Player wins 5, 2 pushes

e. Player wins 7, dealer wins 13

12. a. $7, $3, $12

b. Purchase: 0.00–0.25, 0.25–0.70, 0.70–1.00
Labor: 0.00–0.10, 0.10–0.35, 0.35–0.70, 0.70–1.00
Transportation: 0.00–0.75, 0.75–1.00

c. $5

d. $7

e. Provide probability profit less than $5/unit

14. Selected cell formulas for the worksheet shown in Figure F15.14 are as follows:

Cell	Formula
B13	=$C$7+RAND()*($C$8−$C$7)
C13	=NORMINV(RAND(),$G$7,$G$8)
D13	=($C$3−B13)*C13−$C$4

a. The mean profit should be approximately $6000; simulation results will vary with most simulations having a mean profit between $5500 and $6500

FIGURE F15.14 WORKSHEET FOR THE MADEIRA MANUFACTURING COMPANY

	A	B	C	D	E	F	G	H
1	Madeira Manufacturing Company							
2								
3	Selling Price per Unit		$50					
4	Fixed Cost		$30,000					
5								
6	Variable Cost (Uniform Distribution)				Demand (Normal Distribution)			
7	Smallest Value		$16		Mean		1200	
8	Largest Value		$24		Standard Deviation		300	
9								
10	Simulation trials							
11		Variable						
12	Trial	Cost per Unit	Demand	Profit				
13	1	$17.81	788	($4,681)				
14	2	$18.86	1078	$3,580				
15								

b. 120 to 150 of the 500 simulation trials should show a loss; thus, the probability of a loss should be between 0.24 and 0.30

c. This project appears too risky

16. a. About 36% of simulation runs will show $130,000 as the winning bid

b. $150,000; $10,000

c. Recommended $140,000

18. Selected cell formulas for the worksheet shown in Figure F15.18 are as follows:

Cell	Formula
B11	=$C$4 + RAND()*($C$5−$C$4)
C11	=NORMINV(RAND(),$H$4,$H$5)
D11	=MAX(B11:C11)
G11	=COUNTIF(D11:D1010,"<750")
H11	=G11/COUNT(D11:D1010)

FIGURE F15.18 WORKSHEET FOR THE CONTRACTOR BIDDING

	A	B	C	D	E	F	G	H	I
1	Contractor Bidding								
2									
3	Contractor A (Uniform Distribution)					Contractor B (Normal Distribution)			
4	Smallest Value		$600			Mean		$700	
5	Largest Value		$800			Standard Deviation		$50	
6									
7									
8									
9									
10	Simulation					Results			
11		Contractor	Contractor	Highest		Contractor's	Number	Probability	
12	Trial	A's Bid	B's Bid	Bid		Bid	of Wins	of Winning	
13	1	$673.00	$720	$720		750	629	0.629	
14	2	$757.00	$655	$757		775	824	0.824	
15	3	$706	$791	$791		785	887	0.887	
16	4	$638	$677	$677					
17									

a. $750,000 should win roughly 600 to 650 of the 1000 times; the probability of winning the bid should be between 0.60 and 0.65

b. The probability of $775,000 winning should be roughly 0.82, and the probability of $785,000 winning should be roughly 0.88; a contractor's bid of $775,000 is recommended

20. a. Results vary with each simulation run

Approximate results: 50,000 provided $230,000

                60,000 provided $190,000

                70,000 less than $100,000

b. Recommend 50,000 units

c. Roughly 0.75

22. Very poor operation; some customers wait 30 minutes or more

24. b. Waiting time approximately 0.8 minutes

c. 30% to 35% of customers have to wait

Chapter 16

2. a. 0.82

b. $\pi_1 = 0.5, \pi_2 = 0.5$

c. $\pi_1 = 0.6, \pi_2 = 0.4$

3. a. 0.10 as given by the transition probability

b. $\pi_1 = 0.90\pi_1 + 0.30\pi_2$ (1)

$\pi_2 = 0.10\pi_1 + 0.70\pi_2$ (2)

$\pi_1 + \pi_2 = 1$ (3)

Using (1) and (3),

$$0.10\pi_1 - 0.30\pi_2 = 0$$
$$0.10\pi_1 - 0.30(1 - \pi_1) = 0$$
$$0.10\pi_1 - 0.30 + 0.30\pi_1 = 0$$
$$0.40\pi_1 = 0.30$$
$$\pi_1 = 0.75$$
$$\pi_2 = (1 - \pi_1) = 0.25$$

4. a. $\pi_1 = 0.92, \pi_2 = 0.08$

b. $85

6. a.

	City	Suburbs
City	0.98	0.02
Suburbs	0.01	0.99

b. $\pi_1 = 0.333, \pi_2 = 0.667$

c. City will decrease from 40% to 33%; suburbs will increase from 60% to 67%

7. a. $\pi_1 = 0.85\pi_1 + 0.20\pi_2 + 0.15\pi_3$ (1)

$\pi_2 = 0.10\pi_1 + 0.75\pi_2 + 0.10\pi_3$ (2)

$\pi_3 = 0.05\pi_1 + 0.05\pi_2 + 0.75\pi_3$ (3)

$\pi_1 + \pi_2 + \pi_3 = 1$ (4)

Using (1), (2), and (4) provides three equations with three unknowns; solving provides $\pi_1 = 0.548, \pi_2 = 0.286$, and $\pi_3 = 0.166$

b. 16.6% as given by π_3

c. Quick Stop should take

$667 - 0.548(1000) = 119$ Murphy's customers

and $333 - 0.286(1000) = \underline{47}$ Ashley's customers

Total   166 Quick Stop customers

It will take customers from Murphy's and Ashley's

8. a. MDA

b. $\pi_1 = \frac{1}{3}, \pi_2 = \frac{2}{3}$

10. $3 - 1(0.59), 4 - 1(0.52)$

11. $I = \begin{bmatrix} 1 & 0 \\ 0 & 1 \end{bmatrix}$ $Q = \begin{bmatrix} 0.25 & 0.25 \\ 0.05 & 0.25 \end{bmatrix}$

$(I - Q) = \begin{bmatrix} 0.75 & -0.25 \\ -0.05 & 0.75 \end{bmatrix}$

$N = (I - Q)^{-1} = \begin{bmatrix} 1.3636 & 0.4545 \\ 0.0909 & 1.3636 \end{bmatrix}$

$NR = \begin{bmatrix} 1.3636 & 0.4545 \\ 0.0909 & 1.3636 \end{bmatrix} \begin{bmatrix} 0.5 & 0.0 \\ 0.5 & 0.2 \end{bmatrix} = \begin{bmatrix} 0.909 & 0.091 \\ 0.727 & 0.273 \end{bmatrix}$

$BNR = \begin{bmatrix} 4000 & 5000 \end{bmatrix} \begin{bmatrix} 0.909 & 0.091 \\ 0.727 & 0.273 \end{bmatrix} = \begin{bmatrix} 7271 & 1729 \end{bmatrix}$

Estimate $1729 in bad debts

12. 3580 will be sold eventually; 1420 will be lost

14. a. Graduate and drop out

b. $P(\text{Drop Out}) = 0.15, P(\text{Sophomore}) = 0.10$, $P(\text{Junior}) = 0.75$

c. 0.706, 0.294

d. Yes; $P(\text{Graduate}) = 0.54$

$P(\text{Drop Out}) = 0.46$

e. 1479 (74%) will graduate

Chapter 17

2. a. Let x_1 = number of shares of AGA Products purchased

x_2 = number of shares of Key Oil purchased

To obtain an annual return of exactly 9%:

$$0.06(50)x_1 + 0.10(100)x_2 = 0.09(50,000)$$
$$3x_1 + 10x_2 = 4500$$

To have exactly 60% of the total investment in Key Oil:

$$100x_2 = 0.60(50,000)$$
$$x_2 = 300$$

Therefore, we can write the goal programming model as follows:

Min $P_1(d_1^-) + P_2(d_2^+)$

s.t.

$50x_1 + 100x_2$ $\leq 50,000$ Funds available

$3x_1 + 10x_2 - d_1^+ + d_1^- = 4,500$ P_1 goal

$x_2 - d_2^+ + d_2^- = 300$ P_2 goal

$x_1, x_2, d_1^+, d_1^-, d_2^+, d_2^- \geq 0$

b. In the following graphical solution, $x_1 = 250$ and $x_2 = 375$

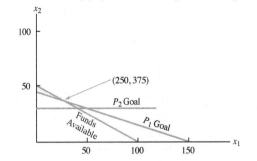

4. a. Min $P_1(d_1^-) + P_1(d_2^+) + P_2(d_3^-) + P_2(d_4^-) + P_3(d_5^-)$

    s.t.

$$20x_1 + 30x_2 - d_1^+ + d_1^- = 4800$$
$$20x_1 + 30x_2 - d_2^+ + d_2^- = 6000$$
$$x_1 \quad\quad - d_3^+ + d_3^- = 100$$
$$x_2 - d_4^+ + d_4^- = 120$$
$$x_1 + x_2 \quad - d_5^+ + d_5^- = 300$$

x_1, x_2, all deviation variables ≥ 0

b. $x_1 = 120, x_2 = 120$

6. a. Let $x_1 =$ number of letters mailed to group 1 customers
$x_2 =$ number of letters mailed to group 2 customers
Min $P_1(d_1^-) + P_1(d_2^+) + P_2(d_3^+)$

    s.t.

$$x_1 \quad\quad - d_1^+ + d_1^- = 40{,}000$$
$$x_2 - d_2^+ + d_2^- = 50{,}000$$
$$x_1 + x_2 - d_3^+ + d_3^- = 70{,}000$$

x_1, x_2, all deviation variables ≥ 0

b. $x_1 = 40{,}000, x_2 = 50{,}000$

c. Optimal solution does not change

8. a. Min $d_1^- + d_1^+ + e_1^- + e_1^+ + d_2^- + d_2^+ + e_2^- + e_2^+ + d_3^- + d_3^+ + e_3^- + e_3^+$

    s.t.

$$x_1 \quad\quad + d_1^- - d_1^+ = 1$$
$$x_2 + e_1^- - e_1^+ = 7$$
$$x_1 \quad\quad + d_2^- - d_2^+ = 5$$
$$x_2 + e_2^- - e_2^+ = 9$$
$$x_1 \quad\quad + d_3^- - d_3^+ = 6$$
$$x_2 + e_3^- - e_3^+ = 2$$

all variables ≥ 0

b. $x_1 = 5, x_2 = 7$

9. Scoring calculations

Criteria	Analyst Chicago	Accountant Denver	Auditor Houston
Career advancement	35	20	20
Location	10	12	8
Management	30	25	35
Salary	28	32	16
Prestige	32	20	24
Job security	8	10	16
Enjoyment of the work	28	20	20
Totals	171	139	139

The analyst position in Chicago is recommended

10. 178, 184, 151
Marysville

12. 170, 168, 190, 183
Handover College

14. a. 220 Bowrider (194)
b. 240 Sundancer (144)

16. Step 1: Column totals are $^{17}/_4$, $^{31}/_{21}$, and 12
Step 2:

Style	Accord	Saturn	Cavalier
Accord	$^4/_{17}$	$^7/_{31}$	$^4/_{12}$
Saturn	$^{12}/_{17}$	$^{21}/_{31}$	$^7/_{12}$
Cavalier	$^1/_{17}$	$^3/_{31}$	$^1/_{12}$

Step 3:

Style	Accord	Saturn	Cavalier	Row Average
Accord	0.235	0.226	0.333	0.265
Saturn	0.706	0.677	0.583	0.656
Cavalier	0.059	0.097	0.083	0.080

Consistency Ratio
Step 1:

$$0.265\begin{bmatrix}1\\3\\\frac14\end{bmatrix} + 0.656\begin{bmatrix}\frac13\\1\\\frac17\end{bmatrix} + 0.080\begin{bmatrix}4\\7\\1\end{bmatrix}$$

$$\begin{bmatrix}0.265\\0.795\\0.066\end{bmatrix} + \begin{bmatrix}0.219\\0.656\\0.094\end{bmatrix} + \begin{bmatrix}0.320\\0.560\\0.080\end{bmatrix} = \begin{bmatrix}0.802\\2.007\\0.239\end{bmatrix}$$

Step 2: $0.802/0.265 = 3.028$
$2.007/0.656 = 3.062$
$0.239/0.080 = 3.007$
Step 3: $\lambda_{max} = (3.028 + 3.062 + 3.007)/3 = 3.032$
Step 4: CI $= (3.032 - 3)/2 = 0.016$
Step 5: CR $= 0.016/0.58 = 0.028$
Because CR $= 0.028$ is less than 0.10, the degree of consistency exhibited in the pairwise comparison matrix for style is acceptable

18. a. 0.724, 0.193, 0.083
b. CR $= 0.057$, yes

20. a.

Flavor	A	B	C
A	1	3	2
B	$\frac13$	1	5
C	$\frac12$	$\frac15$	1

b. Step 1: Column totals are $^{11}/_6$, $^{21}/_5$, and 8

Step 2:

Flavor	A	B	C
A	$\frac{6}{11}$	$\frac{15}{21}$	$\frac{2}{8}$
B	$\frac{2}{11}$	$\frac{5}{21}$	$\frac{5}{8}$
C	$\frac{3}{11}$	$\frac{1}{21}$	$\frac{1}{8}$

Step 3:

Flavor	A	B	C	Row Average
A	0.545	0.714	0.250	0.503
B	0.182	0.238	0.625	0.348
C	0.273	0.048	0.125	0.148

c. Step 1:

$$0.503\begin{bmatrix}1\\ \frac{1}{3}\\ \frac{1}{2}\end{bmatrix} + 0.348\begin{bmatrix}3\\ 1\\ \frac{1}{5}\end{bmatrix} + 0.148\begin{bmatrix}2\\ 5\\ 1\end{bmatrix}$$

$$\begin{bmatrix}0.503\\ 0.168\\ 0.252\end{bmatrix} + \begin{bmatrix}1.044\\ 0.348\\ 0.070\end{bmatrix} + \begin{bmatrix}0.296\\ 0.740\\ 0.148\end{bmatrix} = \begin{bmatrix}1.845\\ 1.258\\ 0.470\end{bmatrix}$$

Step 2: $1.845/0.503 = 3.668$
$1.258/0.348 = 3.615$
$0.470/0.148 = 3.123$
Step 3: $\lambda_{max} = (3.668 + 3.615 + 3.123)/3 = 3.469$
Step 4: CI $= (3.469 - 3)/2 = 0.235$
Step 5: CR $= 0.235/0.58 = 0.415$
Because CR $= 0.415$ is greater than 0.10, the individual's judgments are not consistent

22. a.

	D	S	N
D	1	$\frac{1}{4}$	$\frac{1}{7}$
S	4	1	$\frac{1}{3}$
N	7	3	1

b. 0.080, 0.265, 0.656
c. CR $= 0.028$, yes

24. Criteria: Yield and Risk
Step 1: Column totals are 1.5 and 3
Step 2:

	Yield	Risk	Priority
Yield	0.667	0.667	0.667
Risk	0.333	0.333	0.333

With only two criteria, CR $= 0$; no need to compute CR
Preceding calculations for Yield and Risk provide

Stocks	Yield Priority	Risk Priority
CCC	0.750	0.333
SRI	0.250	0.667

Overall Priorities:
CCC $0.667(0.750) + 0.333(0.333) = 0.611$
SRI $0.667(0.250) + 0.333(0.667) = 0.389$
CCC is preferred

26. a. Criterion: 0.608, 0.272, 0.120
Price: 0.557, 0.123, 0.320
Sound: 0.137, 0.239, 0.623
Reception: 0.579, 0.187, 0.046
b. 0.446, 0.162, 0.392
System A is preferred

index

CPSIA information can be obtained
at www.ICGtesting.com
Printed in the USA
BVHW072123271120
594401BV00005B/66

9 781111 212605